Exploring Science

How Science Works

8

Series Editor:
Mark Levesley

Penny Johnson
Steve Gray
Iain Brand
Mike O'Neill

PEARSON
Longman

Edinburgh Gate
Harlow, Essex

This book also includes

Active Book

Contents

How to use this book

8Ia Keep your cool

HowScienceWorks

Humans live in many different environments all over the world. Some places where humans live are very hot, and some are very cold.

⚠ Innuit people can live in very cold climates, because their clothing and homes help to keep them warm.

⚠ The clothes that these Tuareg men are wearing help to keep them cool.

The temperature of the human body is 37°C. If the inside of our body gets more than a few degrees warmer or cooler than this, we die. Our bodies have ways of keeping us at the right temperature, such as sweating and shivering. However, we cannot live in very hot or very cold places without helping our bodies to stay at the right temperature. We do this by wearing clothes, which slow down the transfer of heat energy between our bodies and our surroundings. We also use buildings to shelter from heat or cold.

1 How do you measure the temperature of something?
2 Could humans live in the UK without clothes? Explain your answer.
3 a Which materials do you think are best at keeping you warm?
   b Explain why you think these materials are best.
4 A flask can keep hot drinks hot. Explain why it can also keep cold drinks cold.

⚠ Firefighters wear protective clothing to help them to survive in burning buildings. The manufacturers of the clothing test it using dummies like 'Pyroman'.

●●●119

Each unit starts with a 'How Science Works' page. This introduces some of the ideas that you will learn more about, by making you think about a real-life situation.

Timeline boxes tell you about how the work of scientists has developed over time.

Photo D shows **pond dipping** – taking samples of water organisms by putting a net or jar into parts of a pond.

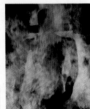

When fishing boats use nets, it is like pond dipping. Marjorie Courtenay-Latimer (1907–2004) worked for a museum in Cape Town, South Africa. She regularly inspected the fish that the boats caught. While doing this on 23rd December 1938, she found a coelacanth – a fish thought to have died out 80 million years ago!

Key words for the page are in bold. You can look up the meaning of these in the glossary on pages 175–181 of the book.

Photo F shows a **pitfall trap**. This is a container buried in the ground. Animals fall into it. This is most often used for small animals.

To study animal tracks and footprints scientists may make plaster casts of the prints. The casts in photo G are supposed to come from undiscovered giant apes living in America.

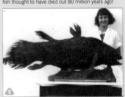

Fact boxes contain fascinating facts to think about.

3 a How would you collect samples of animals living in trees?
   b How would you collect small animals that crawl along the ground?
4 How is fishing with nets like pond dipping?
5 What evidence do you think scientists had for thinking that coelacanths had become extinct?
6 The evidence for communities and populations collected using samples from existing habitats is much more reliable than evidence from fossils. Suggest reasons why.

I CAN...
o use different ways of collecting evidence for communities and populations.

●●●●55

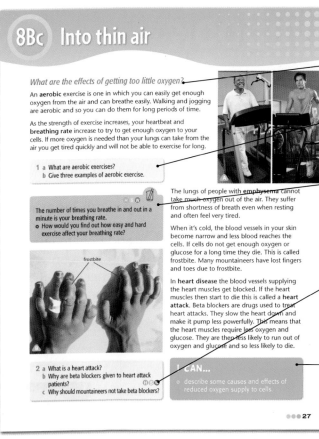

8Bc Into thin air

What are the effects of getting too little oxygen?

An **aerobic** exercise is one in which you can easily get enough oxygen from the air and can breathe easily. Walking and jogging are aerobic and so you can do them for long periods of time.

As the strength of exercise increases, your heartbeat and **breathing rate** increase to try to get enough oxygen to your cells. If more oxygen is needed than your lungs can take from the air you get tired quickly and will not be able to exercise for long.

1 a What are aerobic exercises?
  b Give three examples of aerobic exercise.

The number of times you breathe in and out in a minute is your breathing rate.
○ How would you find out how easy and hard exercise would affect your breathing rate?

frostbite

The lungs of people with **emphysema** cannot take much oxygen out of the air. They suffer from shortness of breath even when resting and often feel very tired.

When it's cold, the blood vessels in your skin become narrow and less blood reaches the cells. If cells do not get enough oxygen or glucose for a long time they die. This is called frostbite. Many mountaineers have lost fingers and toes due to frostbite.

In **heart disease** the blood vessels supplying the heart muscles get blocked. If the heart muscles then start to die this is called a **heart attack**. Beta blockers are drugs used to treat heart attacks. They slow the heart down and make it pump less powerfully. This means that the heart muscles require less oxygen and glucose. They are then less likely to run out of oxygen and glucose and so less likely to die.

2 a What is a heart attack?
  b Why are beta blockers given to heart attack patients?
  c Why should mountaineers not take beta blockers?

I CAN...
○ describe some causes and effects of reduced oxygen supply to cells.

●●● 27

You should be able [...] by the time you have fin[...]

Questions are spread throughout [...] can answer them as you go through t[...]

Practical boxes give you ideas for investigations and practical work. Sometimes there is a picture to give you ideas for planning your investigation.

Where you see this How Science Works icon, it means that the question or piece of text is about practical or enquiry skills, how science has changed over time, or how science is used and applied in real life.

I can... boxes help you to assess what you've learned and check your progress.

Each unit ends with a 'How Science Works' page. Here you can apply what you've learned to a real-life situation.

These give you extra information about the topic.

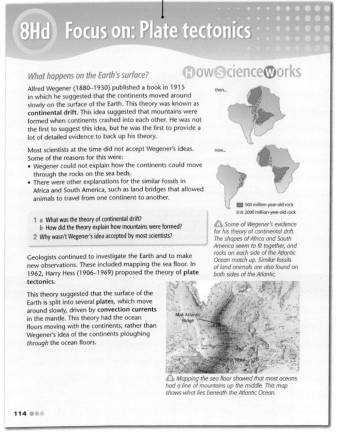

8Hd Focus on: Plate tectonics

⊕ow⊜cience⊛orks

What happens on the Earth's surface?

Alfred Wegener (1880–1930) published a book in 1915 in which he suggested that the continents moved around slowly on the surface of the Earth. This theory was known as **continental drift**. This idea suggested that mountains were formed when continents crashed into each other. He was not the first to suggest this idea, but he was the first to provide a lot of detailed evidence to back up his theory.

Most scientists at the time did not accept Wegener's ideas. Some of the reasons for this were:
• Wegener could not explain how the continents could move through the rocks on the sea beds.
• There were other explanations for the similar fossils in Africa and South America, such as land bridges that allowed animals to travel from one continent to another.

1 a What was the theory of continental drift?
  b How did the theory explain how mountains were formed?
2 Why wasn't Wegener's idea accepted by most scientists?

Geologists continued to investigate the Earth and to make new observations. These included mapping the sea floor. In 1962, Harry Hess (1906–1969) proposed the theory of **plate tectonics**.

This theory suggested that the surface of the Earth is split into several **plates**, which move around slowly, driven by **convection currents** in the mantle. This theory had the ocean floors moving *with* the continents, rather than Wegener's idea of the continents ploughing *through* the ocean floors.

then...

now...

▬ 500 million-year-old rock
≡ 2000 million-year-old rock

⚠ Some of Wegener's evidence for his theory of continental drift. The shapes of Africa and South America seem to fit together, and rocks on each side of the Atlantic Ocean match up. Similar fossils of land animals are also found on both sides of the Atlantic.

Mid-Atlantic Ridge

⚠ Mapping the sea floor showed that most oceans had a line of mountains up the middle. This map shows what lies beneath the Atlantic Ocean.

114 ●●●

If you need to find information about something, use the **index** on pages 183–184.

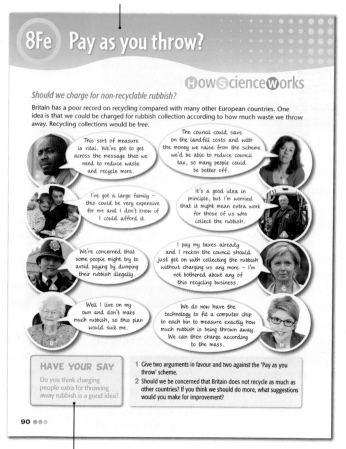

8Fe Pay as you throw?

⊕ow⊜cience⊛orks

Should we charge for non-recyclable rubbish?

Britain has a poor record on recycling compared with many other European countries. One idea is that we could be charged for rubbish collection according to how much waste we throw away. Recycling collections would be free.

This sort of measure is vital. We've got to get across the message that we need to reduce waste and recycle more.

The council could save on the landfill costs and, with the money we raise from the scheme we'd be able to reduce council tax, so many people could be better off.

I've got a large family – this could be very expensive for me and I don't know if I could afford it.

It's a good idea in principle, but I'm worried that it might mean extra work for those of us who collect the rubbish.

We're concerned that some people might try to avoid paying by dumping their rubbish illegally.

I pay my taxes already and I reckon the council should just get on with collecting the rubbish without charging us any more – I'm not bothered about any of this recycling business.

Well I live on my own and don't make much rubbish, so this plan would suit me.

We do now have the technology to fit a computer chip to each bin to measure exactly how much rubbish is being thrown away. We can then charge according to the mass.

HAVE YOUR SAY

Do you think charging people extra for throwing away rubbish is a good idea?

1 Give two arguments in favour and two against the 'Pay as you throw' scheme.
2 Should we be concerned that Britain does not recycle as much as other countries? If you think we should do more, what suggestions would you make for improvement?

90 ●●●

The **Have your say box** gives you an issue for a debate or discussion.

How to use this ActiveBook

Click on this tab to find all the electronic files on the ActiveBook.

Click this tab to see all the key words and what they mean. You can read them or you can click 'play' and listen to someone else read them out for you, to help with pronunciation.

Click on this tab at any time to search for help on how to use the ActiveBook.

Click on a section of the page and it will magnify, so that you can read it easily on screen. You can also zoom in on photos and diagrams on the page.

All of the questions in your book come with a level and some example answers, so you can see exactly how you're doing and how to improve. These are on your teacher's CD-ROM version of the book.

Click on any of the words in **bold** to see a box with the word and what it means. You can read them or you can click 'play' and listen to someone else read them out for you to help with pronunciation.

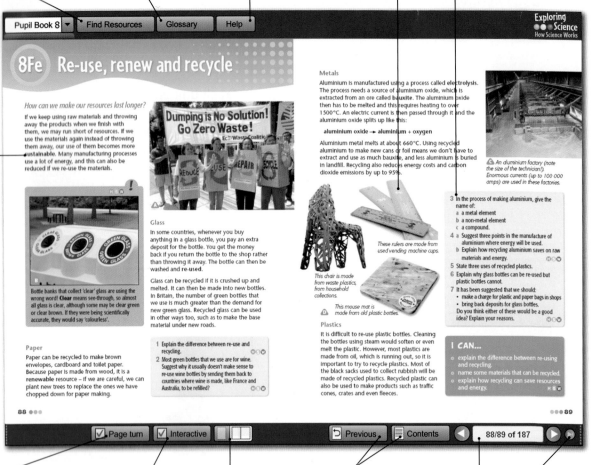

You can choose to see the pages of the book turn, or not.

Click this button to see all the links to electronic files. If you don't want to see these links you can return to book view.

Click these buttons to view the page as a single page or a double page.

Click here to return to the contents page, or go back to the start of the unit.

You can turn to one page at a time, or you can type in the number of the page and go straight to that page. You can go to the end of the book by clicking ▶|.

Ⓗow Ⓢcience Ⓦorks

Health experts are worried that children are eating too many unhealthy foods, which makes them fat. The experts are trying to get young people to eat more healthily.

The Office of Communications (Ofcom) controls what can be broadcast on radio and television. Health experts helped to persuade Ofcom that advertising unhealthy foods on TV was part of the problem. In 2007 Ofcom banned adverts for unhealthy foods from being shown during children's TV programmes.

In April 2007, scientists at Liverpool University carried out an investigation to see if the ban might have an effect. They took 60 children and showed them either food adverts followed by a cartoon, or toy adverts followed by a cartoon. The children were then offered some food. The scientists found that the children who had seen the food adverts ate about twice as much as those who had seen the toy adverts.

Ⓑ *None of these foods can be advertised on children's TV.*

Ⓒ *Children taking part in the investigation at Liverpool University.*

1 a What theory did health experts use to help explain why some children ate too many unhealthy foods?
   b How did scientists at Liverpool University test this theory?
   c Do the results from this investigation provide evidence for or against this theory?

2 a Think up another theory that might explain why children are generally fatter today than they were 40 years ago.
   b Briefly describe how you would test your theory.

3 What do you think the foods that cannot be advertised on children's TV contain?

What does our food contain?

In science, the word **diet** means 'what you eat'. Your food provides **raw materials** for your body, which are needed for:
• energy (to move, etc.)   • growth and repair   • health.

Packaged foods have **nutrition information** labels. Look at the left-hand column of label A and you will see the names of the things in the food. Apart from energy, which is not a substance, the other things are food substances that your body needs.

NUTRITION INFORMATION

TYPICAL VALUES	PER 100g OF PRODUCT	PER AVERAGE SLICE (43.2g)	GUIDELINE DAILY AMOUNTS ADULTS
ENERGY - kJ	982 kJ	424 kJ	
- kcal (Calories)	232 kcal	100 kcal	
PROTEIN	10.9g	4.7g	
CARBOHYDRATE	38.4g	16.6g	2000
of which sugars	2.9g	1.3g	45g
FAT	3.9g	1.7g	230g
of which saturates	0.8g	0.3g	90g
mono-unsaturates	1.2g	0.5g	70g
polyunsaturates	1.7g	0.7g	20g
FIBRE	6.3g	2.7g	
SODIUM	0.39g	0.17g	24g
SALT	0.98g	0.42g	2.4g
			6g

Under warm conditions storage life will be reduced. If freezing, freeze on day of purchase. For 'Best Before' date see bag closure or label.

INGRED
Wholemeal Flour, Water, Malted Sunflower Seeds (2%), Yeast, Wh Sugar, Salt, Barley, Emulsifiers E Preservative Calcium Propionate growth), Flour Treatment Agent /

ALLERGY
This product contains wheat glut This product is produced in a bak Not suitable for sesame allergy s

CUSTOME
FREEPHONE 0800 243684 Monday to Friday from 9.00am (Answerphone at all other time We welcome comments from o Please feel free to call us. You affected.
WARBURTONS LIMITED, HEREFC BOLTON BL1 8JB

Visit us at www.war

A

Nutrition labels were introduced in 1980. They have changed over the years as we have wanted to know more about our food. One of the latest changes has been to clearly show any substances to which people can be allergic (e.g. nuts). The Food Standards Agency is in charge of making sure that the labels are correct.

Carbohydrates, fats, proteins, vitamins and **minerals** are all **nutrients**. Nutrients are food substances that provide raw materials for the body. We also need **fibre** and water in our diets.

Fibre is made of plant cell walls. Our bodies cannot use it but eating it helps to keep our intestines clean and healthy. It also stops our intestines getting blocked up (**constipation**). A good source of fibre is wholemeal bread.

There's a tastier way to a healthier heart. But don't thank us. Thank Wholegrain Goodness.

To find out how wholegrain can help your heart, email me:
jonathan-warburton@warburtonsbakery.co.uk

B BAKERS BORN & BRED

1 What do scientists mean by the word 'diet'?

2 a Look at label A. List the six food substances shown. Ⓗ Ⓢ Ⓦ
   b If you add up the masses of each food substance in the left-hand column, they do not come to 100 g. The rest of the mass is water. Ignoring the minerals, work out how much water there is in 100 g of the bread.

3 You are in charge of marketing a new breakfast cereal called FullBran, which contains a lot of fibre. Write a slogan for a newspaper advertisement. Ⓗ Ⓢ Ⓦ

About 65% of a person is water! Water dissolves things so that they can be carried around the body. It also fills up cells so that they hold their shapes and cools you down when you sweat. You must drink lots of water each day to stay healthy.

4 a Which food substances are nutrients?
  b What other substances do you need in your diet?
  c What are these other substances needed for?

Scientists at the Food Standards Agency test foods to make sure they contain what their packets claim they contain. They use tests like these:

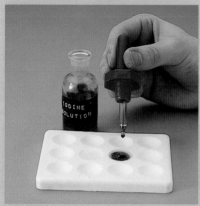

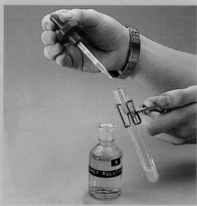

C **Starch** (a carbohydrate): Add two drops of iodine solution to a food sample. If there is starch you will see a blue/black colour.

D Protein: Place a food sample in a test tube to a depth of about 1 cm. Add five drops of Biuret solution. If there is protein you will see a purple colour within a few minutes.

E Fat: Rub a small dry food sample on some white paper. Hold the paper up to the light. Fat leaves a greasy mark.

F

parmesan cheese

How would you test the foods in photo F to see which nutrients they contained? (The tests for starch and protein need the food sample to be mixed with an equal volume of water.)

'Garden of Life' fibre bars were stopped from being sold in 2007. They were advertised as 'dairy free' but food scientists found proteins from milk in them!

5 Gita tested her butter and bread with iodine solution. Which nutrient was she testing for?

6 a **Sugars** are a type of carbohydrate. You can also do food tests for sugars. Which of these foods do you think will have a lot of sugar in them?
    fish   fizzy drink   potato   chocolate   sausages
  b Name one other sort of carbohydrate.

I CAN...

o explain why we need food.
o interpret nutrition labels.
o test foods for starch, proteins and fats. H S W

8Ab Keeping it balanced

What is a balanced diet?

Different foods contain different food substances. No one food contains all the substances that you need and so you need many different foods. If you eat the right amounts of a wide variety of foods you have a **balanced diet**. A food pyramid can help you to plan a balanced diet.

> H S W **!**
>
> Rich people in the sixteenth century had unbalanced diets. They ate lots of meat but very little fruit and vegetables – they thought that fresh fruit was bad for you and regarded food from the ground as being suitable only for the poor.

> 1 What is a balanced diet?

Food substances for energy

Carbohydrates are good sources of energy. Starch and sugar are two kinds of carbohydrate. Starch is found in foods like bread, rice, pasta and potatoes. Sugars are found in many foods (including sweets and cakes).

When carbohydrates are not used up, they can be turned into fat in your body. Fats are also found in foods like milk, cheese, butter and eggs. Fat is stored to be used for energy in the future. Some fat is stored under your skin to help stop heat escaping from your body.

Different people need different amounts of food. You need more food if you are very active and you need more food if you are a boy. The amount of **chemical energy** that a food contains is measured in **kilojoules (kJ)**.

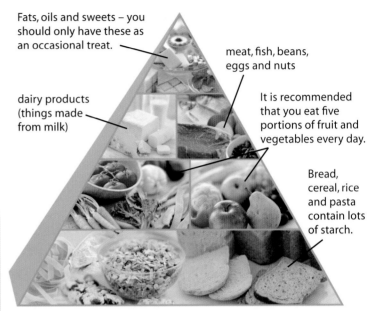

Fats, oils and sweets – you should only have these as an occasional treat.

dairy products (things made from milk)

meat, fish, beans, eggs and nuts

It is recommended that you eat five portions of fruit and vegetables every day.

Bread, cereal, rice and pasta contain lots of starch.

A You should eat more from the groups lower in the pyramid.

B Hard exercise can use up 3–4 grams of carbohydrates each minute. Long distance athletes drink liquids containing glucose during races – although it can be quite hard getting these to a swimmer!

> 2 a Starch and sugar are examples of what food substance?
> b Name two sources of starch.
> c Name two sources of sugar.
> 3 How is fat used in your body?

Table C shows the recommended daily amounts of the different food substances. This sort of information is found on many nutrition information labels.

	Recommended amount for boys in KS3	Recommended amount for girls in KS3	100 g of wholemeal bread contain	100 g of oranges contain	100 g of butter contain
energy	9270 kJ	7920 kJ	920 kJ	150 kJ	3000 kJ
carbohydrate	296 g	246 g	38.4 g	8.5 g	0 g
protein	42 g	41 g	10.3 g	0.8 g	0.5 g
fat	86 g	72 g	2.5 g	0 g	81 g
fibre	18 g	15 g	6.5 g	2.1 g	0 g
vitamin A	600 µg	600 µg	0 µg	5 µg	887 µg
vitamin C	35 mg	35 mg	0 mg	50 mg	0 mg
calcium	1000 mg	800 mg	28 mg	41 mg	15 mg
iron	11 mg	15 mg	3 mg	0.3 mg	0.2 mg

C 1 mg (milligram) = 0.001 g; 1 µg (microgram) = 0.000001 g.

4 Look at table C. One thick slice of wholemeal bread has a mass of 50 g. How much of the following does it contain?
a protein   b fibre
c carbohydrate   H S W

5 a A 50 g slice of wholemeal bread is spread with 10 g of butter. How much chemical energy is in this snack?
b If this snack were tested using iodine solution, what would the result be? H S W

Food substances for growth and repair

Proteins are needed to make new cells to help us to grow and repair our bodies. Proteins are found in foods like meat, fish, eggs, cheese, beans and milk.

D Body builders eat a lot of protein. They often eat special foods that give them extra protein.

Food substances for health

Vitamins and mineral salts (usually just called minerals) are needed in small quantities. They are often found in fruits and vegetables. They help to keep our bodies healthy. For example, iron is used to make red blood cells, and vitamin C helps cells in tissues to stick together properly.

6 a Name two good sources of protein.
b Why do you need proteins in your diet?

7 How many grams of oranges would you need to get the recommended amount of:
a vitamin C   b iron? H S W

8 Which food in the table is the best source of iron?   H S W

9 Do you think you eat a balanced diet? Explain your reasoning.

I CAN...

o explain what a balanced diet is.
o explain why we need carbohydrates, proteins, fats, vitamins and minerals.
o recall good sources of all these food substances.

8Ab Poor diets

What problems can diet cause?

Different diets from different cultures can all be balanced diets.

> 1 Explain why the Indian meal in photograph A is balanced.

A

In some parts of the world, people cannot get enough to eat and they starve. In other areas people get diseases caused by a lack of a particular nutrient.

Eating too much fat can help to cause certain types of cancer and **heart disease**. In heart disease fat blocks the supply of blood to the heart muscle. The muscle starts to die and can cause a painful squeezing feeling in the chest.

If you eat foods containing more energy than you use up you may get fat. Overweight people have more health problems, including heart disease. People who are very fat are said to be **obese**. Some scientists want to ban adverts for very fatty or sugary foods.

Some people become ill by going on 'diets' that are not balanced or contain too little food. People who do not eat enough often feel weak and tired. In some cases this can lead to a disease called anorexia. Fashion companies are often criticised for advertising their clothing using very thin models. Some scientists think that this advertising can change people's behaviour. People learn to associate fashion with being very thin and so go on dangerous diets.

B This boy has a 'big tummy' because he is suffering from a disease called kwashiorkor, caused by a lack of protein.

!

Many cultures eat insects, which are rich in proteins.

C

> 2 For each of these diseases state one cause and one symptom:
>   a heart disease   b anorexia   c kwashiorkor
> 3 Why do you think doctors advise against eating no fat?
> 4 Should adverts for very fatty or sugary foods be banned? Explain your reasoning.   (H)(S)(W)
> 5 The 2006 Madrid Fashion Show banned models who were too thin. What do you think of this idea? Explain your reasoning.   (H)(S)(W)

I CAN...

o explain how too little or too much of a nutrient can cause diseases.
o recognise how advertising affects people's behaviour.   H S (W)

How can diabetes be controlled?

HowScienceWorks

Diabetes causes high levels of glucose to build up in the blood, which can damage the brain, eyes and kidneys. **Insulin** is a chemical made in the **pancreas** that causes cells to take glucose out of the blood. It is released into the blood when the glucose level goes above a certain point. People with 'type I' diabetes cannot make insulin. The bodies of people with 'type II' diabetes do not produce enough insulin or cannot use it properly. Obese people are at risk of developing type II diabetes.

Treatment

Some people with diabetes have to inject themselves with insulin to make sure that their blood glucose does not get too high. Others can control their diabetes by cutting down on the amounts of fatty and sugary foods that they eat.

Discovery

About 2500 years ago an Indian doctor, Susruta, tested for diabetes by seeing if ants were attracted to people's urine. The disease was called 'madhu-meh' or 'sweet urine'.

In 1776, Yorkshire doctor Matthew Dobson (1731–1784) evaporated urine from a diabetic patient and showed that it contained sugar. He also found sugar in the patient's blood.

In 1889, German scientist Oscar Minkowski (1858–1931) was studying **digestion**. In his studies he removed the pancreases from some dogs. The dogs became very ill and one of Minkowski's assistants noticed that ants were attracted to their urine. Minkowski had heard about the ants in ancient India and made the connection.

1 a How can diet help to cause type II diabetes?
  b Someone with type II diabetes eats a glucose tablet. Suggest two ways in which the person's blood glucose levels would become too high.

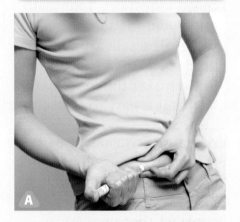
A

2 Why are people with diabetes encouraged to avoid too many sugary foods?
3 Why do you think diabetes causes 'sweet urine'?
4 The text refers to a connection made by Minkowski. What was this connection?

B *Banting won a Nobel Prize for his work on insulin.*

This encouraged other scientists to find out how the pancreas altered the glucose levels in blood. In 1921, Canadian scientist Sir Frederick Banting (1891–1941) and his student Charles Best (1899–1978) finally extracted insulin from pancreases. They used their insulin to successfully reduce glucose levels in the blood of a 14-year-old boy, and so control the boy's diabetes.

What do the parts of the digestive system do?

A process called **digestion** turns food into a form that your body can use. It happens as your food passes down a tube made up of different organs, called the **gut**. Other organs (like the **liver**) also help with digestion. The gut and these other organs make up the **digestive system**.

> 1 What process turns your food into a form that your body can use?
> 2 Look at diagram A. Where does the gut begin and end?

Putting food in your mouth is called **ingestion**. Your teeth grind your food into smaller pieces. The **salivary glands** produce a liquid called **saliva**. Saliva makes the food moist so that it is easy to swallow.

salivary gland

When you swallow, the windpipe is shut off and food goes into the **gullet**. Muscles in the wall of the gullet **contract** (get smaller) to narrow the tube above the food. This pushes food down to the stomach. Muscles in the rest of the gut move food in the same way.

In the **stomach** the food is churned up with strong acid (pH 1–2).

The **appendix** is a small tube. In some animals it helps to digest grass. In humans it has no real job and sometimes gets infected (appendicitis). If this happens the appendix is removed.

The particles that make up food are called **molecules**. Small molecules are **absorbed** (taken into the body) through the wall of the **small intestine**. There is also about 1 kg of bacteria in your small intestine! Some of these are useful (e.g. they make vitamin K). Others are harmful. Some foods contain bacteria that are thought to stop the harmful bacteria causing problems.

Yakult was developed in 1935 by the scientist Dr. Shirota and contains the good bacteria *Lactobacillus casei* Shirota. He found that these bacteria could help keep the gut healthy. And a healthy gut supports your natural defences. We recommend you drink one bottle of Yakult every day. For good health it's important to eat a varied, balanced diet and lead a healthy lifestyle. To find out more, visit our website for information on friendly bacteria and a healthy lifestyle.

B

Food that we cannot digest (e.g. fibre) goes into the **large intestine**, where water is removed. This forms a more solid material called **faeces** (pronounced 'fee-sees'). There are bacteria here too – about 60% of faeces are actually dead bacteria!

Faeces are stored in the **rectum**. They are eventually pushed out of the **anus** in a process called **elimination** or **egestion**.

A

3 What is the job of the large intestine?

4 a List the organs of the gut in the order that food passes through them.

  b How is food pushed along the gut?

  c How long does this take?

  d Name one other organ, not part of the gut, that is part of the digestive system.

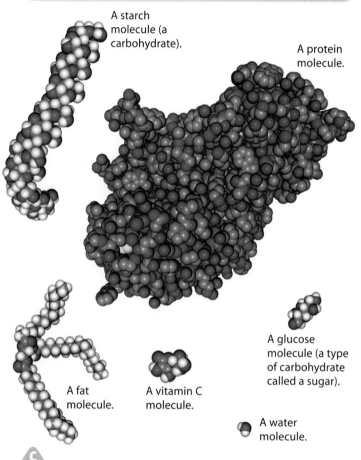

A starch molecule (a carbohydrate).

A protein molecule.

A fat molecule.

A vitamin C molecule.

A glucose molecule (a type of carbohydrate called a sugar).

A water molecule.

6 a Where are food substances absorbed?

  b How do enzymes help your food to be absorbed?

7 a Name one soluble carbohydrate.

  b Name one insoluble carbohydrate.

8 Adverts for Actimel™ claim that it 'helps support your body's defences'. ⒣⒮Ⓦ

  a How do you think it helps?

  b Would this encourage you to buy Actimel™? Explain your answer.

  c Briefly describe a way of testing this claim.

The gut is about 8 m long. The intestines are coiled up so that they can fit inside the body. It normally takes between 24 and 48 hours for food to go through the gut. Fibre in your diet helps this to happen.

The diagrams show models of some molecules found in food. Only molecules of the same size or smaller than glucose can be absorbed by the small intestine.

5 Look at the molecules.

  a Which molecule should form the biggest part of your diet?

  b Which molecules will be absorbed in the small intestine? ⒣⒮Ⓦ

  c From your answer to part b, predict which molecule will be the most easily absorbed. ⒣⒮Ⓦ

  d The molecules that cannot be absorbed are still important for the body. Suggest what has to happen to them so they can be absorbed. ⒣⒮Ⓦ

Most of the food we eat is **insoluble** (it won't dissolve). To make use of our food, most of it needs to be broken apart into smaller, **soluble** substances. This is what happens in digestion. Special chemicals called **enzymes** do this.

Sugars (e.g. glucose), vitamins and minerals are small and soluble in water and so can pass through the wall of the small intestine. Larger insoluble molecules, like starch, fats and proteins, need to be broken up into small, soluble molecules by enzymes.

I CAN...

o recall the parts of the digestive system and their functions.

o explain why enzymes are needed in the gut.

o recognise how models of molecules can be shown.   H S Ⓦ

8Ad Break down

How is food digested?

Many parts of the digestive system produce **digestive juices** that contain enzymes. For instance, digestive juices found in the small intestine contain enzymes that break large insoluble starch molecules into small soluble glucose molecules. The glucose molecules can then be absorbed by the small intestine.

A **model** helps us to think about how complicated things happen. Diagram A shows a model small intestine. Visking tubing is a very thin material containing microscopic holes that only small, soluble molecules can pass through. The inside of the tubing represents the inside of the small intestine. The water around the outside of the tubing represents the blood in the body.

The model small intestine works best if the temperature is about 37 °C. This is because enzymes have a certain temperature that they work best at. The enzymes in humans work best at body temperature (37 °C).

Enzymes in other parts of the gut

All enzymes have a certain pH that they work best at. There are enzymes in saliva that break down starch. These enzymes only work properly at about pH 7, which is the pH in the mouth. They stop working when the food reaches the stomach because the stomach contains hydrochloric acid.

Digestive juices in the stomach contain enzymes that digest proteins. There are more enzymes in the small intestine that break down starch, proteins and fats.

2 a What variables would you need to control if you wanted to see if enzyme supplements make a difference to people's health? Ⓗ Ⓢ Ⓦ
   b What observations would you make?
3 If the food supplement enzymes are to be of any use, they need to survive in the stomach. What pH do they need to be able to survive?
4 The small intestine produces an enzyme called protease.
   a What temperature do you think protease works best at?
   b What food substance do you think protease breaks up?
5 How do small molecules get into the blood?

boiling tube
Visking tubing
water, starch and enzyme mixture
water

Ⓐ

1 a Which food substance is inside the tubing at the start? Ⓗ Ⓢ Ⓦ
   b Which substance would you expect to find in the water after 30 minutes?

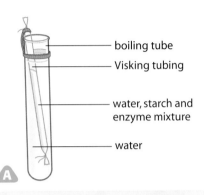

Ⓗ Ⓢ Ⓦ

Some food supplements contain enzymes that are claimed to be good for your health.

Ⓑ

Ⓗ Ⓢ Ⓦ

Amylase is an enzyme found in the small intestine. It breaks down starch. How would you investigate which variables affect how quickly amylase works?

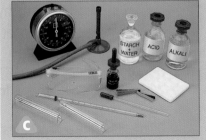

Ⓒ

Models of how enzymes work

The way in which enzymes actually work is extremely complicated so we use models to think about them. A good model tries to represent the known facts about something. A model about digestive enzymes needs to try to represent these facts:

• Enzymes turn large molecules into smaller ones.
• Enzymes do not get used up as they carry out their tasks.
• Enzymes change shape as they work.
• Each enzyme only works on one particular type of molecule.

In 1833, French chemist Anselme Payen (1795–1891) discovered an extract of germinated barley that changed starch into glucose. He called it diastase. It is due to this name that all enzymes end in the suffix '-ase'.

One model imagines that enzymes act like pairs of scissors, cutting through the connections that hold the molecule together.

Another model imagines that they are like a wrench twisting the nut off a bolt.

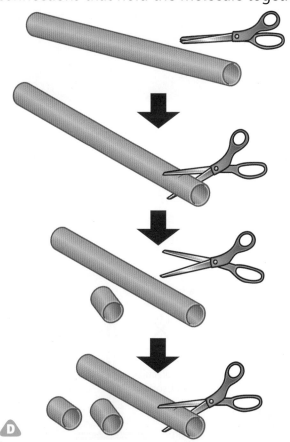

D

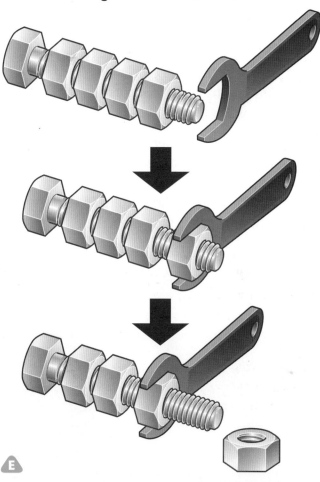

E

6 a What are the strengths of the scissors model? ⒽⓈⓌ
  b What are this model's weak points?
7 a What are the strengths of the spanner model? ⒽⓈⓌ
  b What are this model's weak points?
8 Why are there so many different types of enzymes in the gut?

I CAN...

○ explain what enzymes do.
○ describe the conditions in which enzymes work best.
○ describe and evaluate models to explain how enzymes work. ⒽⓈⓌ

8Ae In the blood

Why is digested food carried around the body?

People with a disease called diabetes need to keep a very careful watch on the amount of a sugar (glucose) that is in their blood. They use a simple blood test to find out.

There are many other blood tests, including checking the levels of vitamins, minerals and a fat called cholesterol. Too much cholesterol can cause health problems like heart disease.

> 1 Jay has been told that his cholesterol level is too high. **H S W**
>   a Suggest one way he could reduce it.
>   b Why may he want to reduce it?

Glucose, vitamins, minerals and fats all come from food. The wall of the small intestine is adapted so these substances are absorbed into the blood quickly: it is very thin and is lined with **villi**. These look like fingers (one finger is called a **villus**) and create a large surface area. The larger the surface area, the faster the substances are absorbed.

A *This boy checks his glucose levels three times a day.*

> **!**
> Villi help to give the small intestine a total surface area of 10 m².

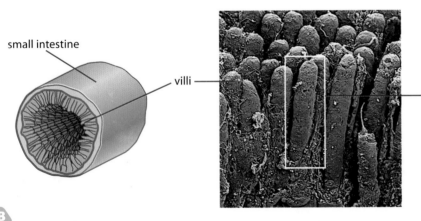

small intestine

villi

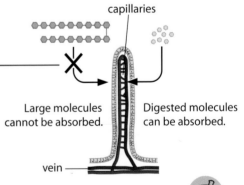

capillaries

Large molecules cannot be absorbed.

Digested molecules can be absorbed.

vein

B

> 2 a We say that digested food is absorbed. What does this mean?
>   b What adaptations does the small intestine have for absorption?

Digested food passes into tiny **blood vessels** called **capillaries** inside the villi. The capillaries join up to a **vein** that carries the blood to the liver. In the liver, poisons are removed before the blood is pumped around the body by the heart.

> **H S W**
> Bath towels have things like villi on them; bed sheets do not. How would you investigate which material absorbs water more quickly?
> ● What do you predict you will find?

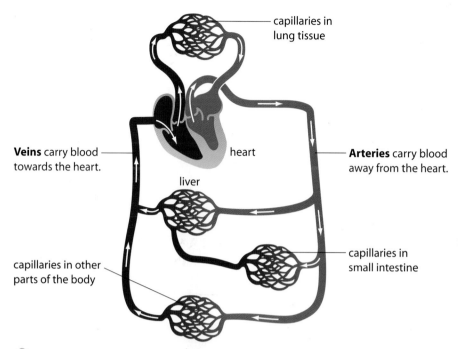

capillaries in lung tissue

Veins carry blood towards the heart.

heart

liver

Arteries carry blood away from the heart.

capillaries in small intestine

capillaries in other parts of the body

C *The heart and blood vessels form the* **circulatory system**.

Tissues in the body contain many capillaries so that cells are never far from a source of digested food. The liquid part of the blood leaks out of the capillaries in tissues and forms **tissue fluid**. This carries dissolved digested food molecules to the cells.

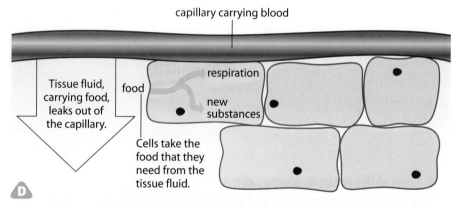

capillary carrying blood

Tissue fluid, carrying food, leaks out of the capillary.

food

respiration

new substances

Cells take the food that they need from the tissue fluid.

D

Cells use glucose to release energy using a chemical reaction called **respiration**. Some of the energy released by respiration is heat energy. This helps us to stay warm. Some of the energy is needed to work muscles so that we can move.

A lot of the energy is used up by all the other chemical reactions that happen. Many of the reactions produce new substances for the body to use. The raw materials for these new substances come from the digested food substances in the blood. The new substances are used to make new cells. New cells help us to grow and repair our bodies.

3 Write down one difference between arteries and veins.

4 What is the circulatory system?

5 A starch molecule is in your small intestine. Write a list of bullet points to describe how the energy in the starch molecule is eventually released inside a muscle cell in your leg.

6 Muscle cells make a carbohydrate called glycogen.
   a Suggest what food substance is needed to make glycogen.
   b How do the muscle cells get the energy needed to make glycogen?

7 People can buy blood-testing kits to test for different things in the blood. Ⓗ Ⓢ Ⓦ
   a Why do you think these kits are becoming more popular?
   b Suggest one problem of using a blood-testing kit.

I CAN...

○ describe how digested food substances enter the circulatory system.
○ recall what digested food is used for.

How **S**cience **W**orks

What are the rules about wording on food packets?

A **health claim** is a statement on a food telling you about the food's good effects on your body. Claims try to get you to change your behaviour and buy the foods. They include things like 'helps aid digestion'. In 2007 the European Union passed a law that said that all health claims must be backed up by scientific evidence.

There are other phrases used on food packaging that may encourage you to buy them. Some, like 'organic' and 'low fat', have strict rules about when they can and cannot be used. An organic product must have been produced using very few chemicals. A low fat product must have less than 3 g of fat per 100 g.

Some phrases have no rules. These include 'light' or 'lite', 'traditional style', 'finest' and 'handmade'.

A

1 Look at the foods in photograph A.
  a Select two of the foods and say how their packaging has been designed to encourage people to buy the foods.
  b Write down two of the health claims on the foods.
  c What do food manufacturers need before they can put a health claim on a packet?
  d Apart from health claims, there are other words on some of the packets shown. Which of these words do you think have rules on their use?
  e Which words do you think have no rules on their use?

2 Look back through this unit and find the other examples of health claims. Write down the ones you find.

8Ba Going for gold

How Science Works

Anne Wafula-Strike is a paralympic athlete. Like all athletes she relies on a range of people to help her achieve her best. Many of these people have scientific backgrounds.

Physiotherapist

A physiotherapist treats an athlete's injuries and tries to prevent them occurring. Physiotherapists also advise athletes on their training so that they can strengthen certain muscles in the correct way without causing injuries.

Sports scientist

A sports scientist monitors the performance of an athlete. He or she often uses machines to measure how well an athlete's body is coping with exercise. Data from the machines helps the sports scientist to design ways to help an athlete improve.

A *Anne Wafula-Strike competing in the 400 metres at the Paralympic World Cup in 2007.*

Engineer

All athletes rely on engineers to design equipment that will help them improve in their sports. Anne's wheelchair is specially designed for her by an engineer.

Dietician

A dietician gives athletes advice on what to eat to make sure that their bodies are in top condition and that they have enough energy.

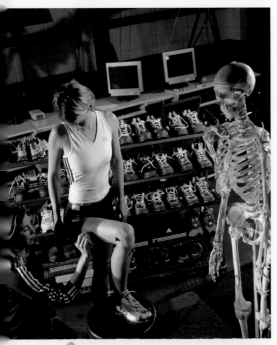

B *This engineer is putting movement sensors on an athlete's leg. These record how changes in shoe design affect the movement of the athlete's joints. The idea is to make shoes that reduce the stress on joints during exercise.*

1 a List four jobs involved with sports that need a knowledge of science.
  b For each job give an example of some science that the person needs to know about.
2 List four items of sports equipment that you think engineers help to design.
3 What sorts of food do you think a dietician would advise Anne to have more of than a non-athlete? Explain your reasons.
4 Daniel Sadler is an able-bodied wheelchair athlete. He is banned from many races. Do you think this is fair or not? Explain your thoughts.

Energy for life

What is respiration?

Dieticians plan diets for athletes so that they eat the right foods to build up muscles and provide the energy they need for their sports. **Glucose** is the molecule that cells need to release energy. Cells need energy to stay alive, to make new substances and to help us move. Most glucose is produced in the body by the **digestion** of **carbohydrates**.

> 1 What do cells use digested food for?
> 2 Why do you think marathon competitors drink glucose drinks rather than eat a food containing carbohydrates? (*Hint*: Think about how long digestion takes.)

Respiration

Sports scientists help athletes to breathe properly so that they can get a lot of air into and out of their lungs. We now know that only part of the air is used in the body. In 1660 Robert Boyle (1627–1691) placed a burning candle in a jar and sucked out all the air. He repeated the experiment with a mouse. Diagram B shows his results.

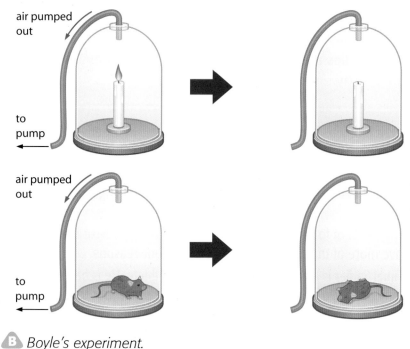

B Boyle's experiment.

A Marathon competitors can pick up glucose drinks on the way. Wheelchair competitors take the drinks with them.

The 'marathon' is named after the battle of Marathon in 490 BCE. After winning the battle, the Greek army sent a messenger called Phidippides to run the 40 km (25 miles) to Athens with the news. Phidippides had already run about 450 km in the previous week and after delivering his message he died. The modern marathon is 26.2 miles, which was set for the 1908 Olympic Games in London. It was the distance between Windsor Castle and King Edward VII's royal box in White City Stadium!

> 3 What do you think Boyle's conclusion from his experiments was? Ⓗ Ⓢ Ⓦ

John Mayow (1641–1679) became Boyle's assistant and did further experiments. He discovered that only a certain part of the air was needed to keep a candle alight and a small animal alive.

4 What evidence did Mayow find to show that only part of the air was needed to keep animals alive? Ⓗ Ⓢ Ⓦ

Later on, scientists like Joseph Priestley (1733–1804) and Antoine Lavoisier (1743–1794) showed that this part of the air was **oxygen**.

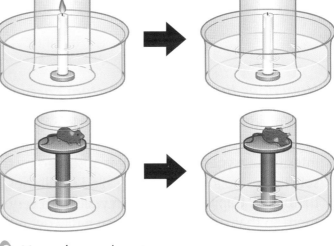
Ⓒ Mayow's experiment.

Today we know that cells use the glucose and oxygen to release energy in a series of chemical reactions called **aerobic respiration** ('aerobic' means 'requiring air').

As well as energy for the cell, respiration also releases heat energy and is like a very controlled form of burning. We can sum up aerobic respiration in a **word equation**:

oxygen + glucose → carbon dioxide + water
reactants   products

 Ⓓ

Ⓗ Ⓢ Ⓦ 📓

All living cells respire, including those in plants and microbes, like yeast. How would you show that respiration will only occur in living yeast cells?
- What would you test for?
- How would you do your test or tests?

Ⓔ

5 Here are three organ systems:
breathing system   circulatory system   digestive system
Which is used for:
  a getting glucose into the blood
  b getting oxygen into the blood
  c getting blood to the cells?

6 a Write out the word equation for aerobic respiration. Ⓗ Ⓢ Ⓦ
  b Write out the word equation for burning glucose. Ⓗ Ⓢ Ⓦ
  c List four ways in which aerobic respiration is like burning. Ⓗ Ⓢ Ⓦ
  d List one way in which they are different. Ⓗ Ⓢ Ⓦ
  e Name one sort of energy released by burning but not by respiration.

7 Two beakers contain peas. Beaker X contains peas that are starting to grow. Beaker Y contains boiled peas. Ⓗ Ⓢ Ⓦ
  a In which beaker will the temperature rise? Explain your reasoning.
  b In which beaker will carbon dioxide be made? Explain your reasoning.

I CAN...

- recall the word equation for aerobic respiration.
- explain the importance of digestion and respiration.
- draw conclusions from historical experiments. Ⓗ Ⓢ Ⓦ

8Bb Round and round

How does the circulatory system carry substances?

(sugar)

Cells need glucose and oxygen to release energy. Glucose from digested carbohydrates is **absorbed** (taken in) by the small intestine. Oxygen from the air is absorbed by the lungs. These substances go into tiny tubes called **capillaries**, where they enter the blood. Capillaries have thin walls with very small holes in them so that small molecules can easily get into and out of them.

A capillary is a type of **blood vessel** – a tube carrying blood pumped by your **heart**. There are two other sorts of larger blood vessels; **arteries** carry blood away from the heart and **veins** carry **blood** to the heart. The heart and blood vessels form the **circulatory system**.

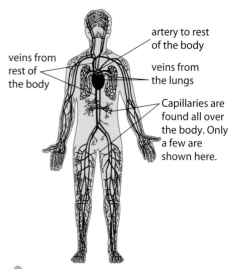

veins from rest of the body

artery to rest of the body

veins from the lungs

Capillaries are found all over the body. Only a few are shown here.

A *The circulatory system.*

Discovering capillaries

In the seventeenth century many people thought that blood poured into organs and was used up. An English doctor called William Harvey (1578–1657) invented a **theory** that said that blood stays inside blood vessels and is not used up. His theory predicted that capillaries must exist, although he could not find them. In 1661 Italian scientist Marcello Malpighi (1628–1694) found capillaries using a microscope.

> 1 a What are capillaries?
> b Why can substances get into and out of capillaries easily?

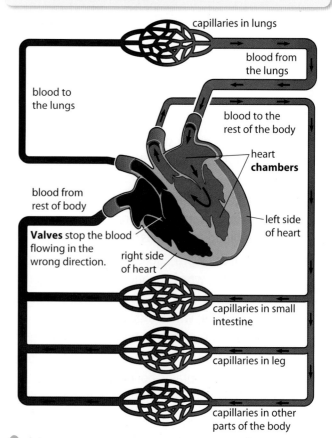

capillaries in lungs

blood from the lungs

blood to the lungs

blood to the rest of the body

heart **chambers**

blood from rest of body

left side of heart

Valves stop the blood flowing in the wrong direction.

right side of heart

capillaries in small intestine

capillaries in leg

capillaries in other parts of the body

> 2 Harvey's theory made a prediction. What was it? ⒽⓈⓌ
> 3 How do you think Malpighi found out about Harvey's work? ⒽⓈⓌ

More about the circulatory system

The right side of your heart receives blood from all over your body and pumps it to your lungs. The left side of your heart receives blood from the lungs and pumps it around the rest of your body. This side is bigger because it has to pump harder to get the blood all the way around your body.

B *There are many branches in the circulatory system. Only a few are shown in this **model**.*

4 a Copy and complete this flowchart to show the route a glucose molecule takes from the small intestine to a leg muscle cell.

b Show the route an oxygen molecule takes from the lungs to a leg muscle cell.

5 a Which side of the heart is bigger?

b Why is this?

c What do the heart valves do?

C An athlete's pulse rate is often measured. It provides a measure of fitness.

To pump your blood, your heart chambers fill with blood and then the muscles in the walls of the heart squeeze the blood out. This is a **heartbeat**. If you press two fingers firmly onto your wrist, you can feel the pumping. This is your **pulse**. Your **pulse rate** is the number of beats you can feel in one minute.

6 a Sonia says 'My pulse rate is 70'. This is not very scientific. What should she say?

b What does a pulse rate tell you?

Oxygen is carried by **red blood cells**. Glucose is dissolved in the blood **plasma** (the liquid part of the blood). Plasma leaks out of the capillaries in your tissues and forms tissue fluid, which flows over the cells. Oxygen can leave red blood cells and dissolve in the tissue fluid. The red blood cells stay inside the capillaries.

7 a Which blood vessels allow substances to travel between the blood and other cells in the body?

b What liquid comes out of these blood vessels?

c Why do you think the red blood cells stay in these blood vessels?

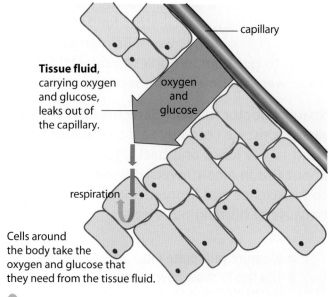

capillary

Tissue fluid, carrying oxygen and glucose, leaks out of the capillary.

oxygen and glucose

respiration

Cells around the body take the oxygen and glucose that they need from the tissue fluid.

D

!

In an average lifetime the heart beats 4 000 000 000 times without stopping.

H S W

How would you find out what effect exercise has on your pulse rate?

I CAN...

o recall that theories make predictions. H S W

o explain how the circulatory system delivers oxygen and glucose to tissues.

How have our ideas about circulation changed? HowScienceWorks

Erasistratus (310 BCE–250 BCE) was a Greek doctor who thought that one half of the heart contained air. Later, another Greek doctor called Galen (c.129–c.200) cut up dead animals (assuming they looked the same inside as humans) and showed that the whole heart contained blood. He cut up many fish, which have two-chambered hearts.

Galen thought that 'nutritive blood' was made by the liver. This sloshed backwards and forwards in veins and was used up by organs. Some of this blood was sucked from the veins by the heart and passed through holes in the **septum** of the heart where it mixed with air to form 'vital blood', which sloshed around in arteries.

Galen was such a brilliant doctor that his ideas were believed by western scientists for 1400 years. Andreas Vesalius (1514–1564) was a Belgian doctor who robbed graves to get human bodies to dissect! He showed that there were no holes in the septum.

Spanish doctor Michael Servetus (1511–1553) also did dissections. He correctly said that blood went from the heart to the lungs and back again. However, he wrote about this in a controversial book about religion and so his science was ignored. He was burned to death because of his religious views.

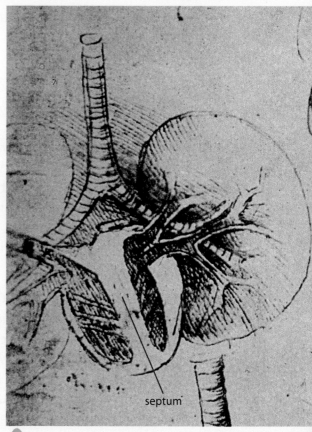

septum

A *An early Leonardo da Vinci (1452–1519) drawing of a heart.*

---

1 a Measure your pulse rate.
  b Use this to show how Harvey worked out that blood was not used up.
2 Why was Servetus' evidence that Galen was wrong ignored?
3 Look at da Vinci's drawing.
  a What is different about this and what we know about heart chambers today?
  b Suggest why da Vinci thought this.

William Harvey (1578–1657) used the scientific method. He asked questions, invented theories, made predictions and then tested those predictions. One theory was that blood was not used up. He found that a human heart contained about 70 cm³ of blood. He multiplied this by the number of heartbeats in a day and found that it was far more blood than the body could possibly make.

Harvey waited over a decade before publishing his theory of circulation in a book in 1628 because he was scared about what others would think of his theories – which went against Galen.

What are the effects of getting too little oxygen?

An **aerobic** exercise is one in which you can easily get enough oxygen from the air and can breathe easily. Walking and jogging are aerobic and so you can do them for long periods of time.

As the strength of exercise increases, your heartbeat and **breathing rate** increase to try to get enough oxygen to your cells. If more oxygen is needed than your lungs can take from the air you get tired quickly and will not be able to exercise for long.

A

1 a What are aerobic exercises?
b Give three examples of aerobic exercise.

H S W

The number of times you breathe in and out in a minute is your breathing rate.
o How would you find out how easy and hard exercise affect your breathing rate?

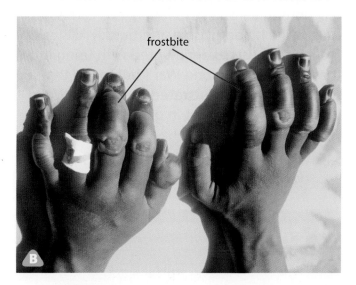

frostbite

B

2 a What is a heart attack?
b Why are beta blockers given to heart attack patients? H S W
c Why should mountaineers not take beta blockers?

The lungs of people with **emphysema** cannot take much oxygen out of the air. They suffer from shortness of breath even when resting and often feel very tired.

When it's cold, the blood vessels in your skin become narrow and less blood reaches the cells. If cells do not get enough oxygen or glucose for a long time they die. This is called frostbite. Many mountaineers have lost fingers and toes due to frostbite.

In **heart disease** the blood vessels supplying the heart muscles get blocked. If the heart muscles then start to die this is called a **heart attack**. Beta blockers are drugs used to treat heart attacks. They slow the heart down and make it pump less powerfully. This means that the heart muscles require less oxygen and glucose. They are then less likely to run out of oxygen and glucose and so less likely to die.

I CAN...

o describe some causes and effects of reduced oxygen supply to cells.

How do some chemicals affect respiration?

Respiring cells absorb the chemicals they need from tissue fluid. Energy is released and waste **carbon dioxide** and water are made. In large amounts carbon dioxide stops aerobic respiration and so is poisonous to cells. It must be removed quickly. It dissolves in the tissue fluid and is carried in the blood plasma back to the lungs to be **excreted**.

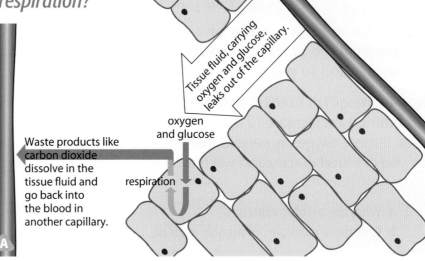

Tissue fluid, carrying oxygen and glucose, leaks out of the capillary.

oxygen and glucose

Waste products like carbon dioxide dissolve in the tissue fluid and go back into the blood in another capillary.

respiration

A

Gas appliances that are not working properly produce carbon monoxide. If you breathe in this gas it sticks to red blood cells and stops them carrying oxygen. It also turns muscle and red blood cells bright red. This makes it useful for packaging meat (the bright red colour lasts a long time and makes the meat look fresh).

1 How does the blood carry carbon dioxide?

2 When you exercise your breathing rate increases. How does this help aerobic respiration to continue to happen? Name two gases in your answer.

3 Doctors examine the skins of people that they think have been killed by carbon monoxide. What colour would the skin be? H S W

4 What are the advantages and disadvantages of packaging meat with carbon monoxide? H S W

Hydrogen cyanide gas stops one of the reactions in aerobic respiration. It is carried to cells in the blood plasma and quickly kills cells. French scientists experimented with using it on the battlefield in World War I but found that it needed to be **concentrated** to work. In World War II the Nazis used it in gas chambers.

5 Why did the Nazis not kill people with hydrogen cyanide in the open air? H S W

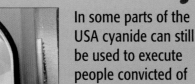

! In some parts of the USA cyanide can still be used to execute people convicted of serious offences.

B A gas chamber in a US prison.

I CAN...

o describe how chemicals are exchanged between cells and blood.

o explain the effects of some poisonous gases.

o identify questionable uses of scientific knowledge. H S W

What happens when the body is short of oxygen?

During exercise, your heart rate increases. Glucose and oxygen need to be supplied quickly to muscle cells and carbon dioxide needs to be rapidly removed. Your breathing rate also increases to take in more oxygen and excrete more carbon dioxide.

Despite these changes, sometimes the body cannot provide the muscles with enough oxygen. The cells need more energy so they start to use **anaerobic respiration**. In this process they break down glucose without oxygen to release energy.

glucose → lactic acid

B Anaerobic respiration.

Anaerobic respiration does not release as much energy as aerobic respiration because not all of the energy is released from each glucose molecule. The lactic acid that is produced still has quite a bit of energy locked up in it. Muscles cannot respire anaerobically for long because lactic acid is poisonous. Too much lactic acid in the muscle cells can also cause cramp.

When you stop exercising hard you continue to pant in order to supply oxygen for aerobic respiration to break down the lactic acid. The amount of oxygen required to do this is called the **oxygen debt**.

A At the end of a hard race, athletes pant and can get cramp in their muscles.

! When people hold their breath, the oxygen in their bodies starts to run out and cells start to use anaerobic respiration more.

C In 2008 David Blaine broke the world record for breath-holding underwater – 17 minutes and 4 seconds.

1 How and why do the heart and breathing rates change during hard exercise?

2 What do you think is meant by the term 'anaerobic'?

3 Give two differences between aerobic and anaerobic respiration.

4 Why is less energy released in anaerobic respiration?

5 a What is meant by an 'oxygen debt'?
  b Why might someone with cramp be given pure oxygen to breathe? Ⓗ Ⓢ Ⓦ

6 What do you think David Blaine does: Ⓗ Ⓢ Ⓦ
  a before holding his breath
  b while holding his breath?

7 Explain your reasoning for your answers to question **6**.

How are gases exchanged in the lungs?

Aerobic respiration needs glucose and oxygen, which are carried in your blood. The **digestive system** gets glucose into the blood. The **breathing system** (or **respiratory system**) gets oxygen into your blood and excretes carbon dioxide from it.

Breathing is when muscles change the size of your lungs. When you **inhale** your lungs get bigger. When you **exhale** your lungs get smaller. The movement of air into and out of your lungs is called **ventilation**.

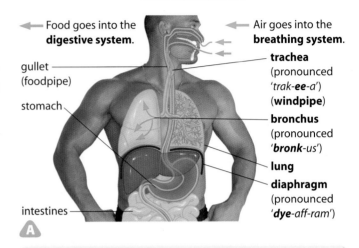

Food goes into the **digestive system**.

Air goes into the **breathing system**.

gullet (foodpipe)

stomach

intestines

trachea (pronounced 'trak-**ee**-a') (**windpipe**)

bronchus (pronounced '**bronk**-us')

lung

diaphragm (pronounced '**dye**-aff-ram')

A

1 a What is ventilation?   b What is breathing?

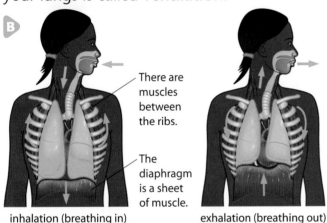

There are muscles between the ribs.

The diaphragm is a sheet of muscle.

inhalation (breathing in)

exhalation (breathing out)

B

Picking up oxygen and getting rid of carbon dioxide in the alveoli is called **gas exchange**. Red blood cells are bright red when carrying oxygen, and dark red/brown when not.

The lungs contain thousands of **air sacs** containing tiny pockets called **alveoli** (pronounced '*al-vee-O-lee*'). These give the lungs a large surface area for absorbing oxygen and excreting carbon dioxide. The alveoli have walls that are only one cell thick. They are surrounded by many capillaries, which also have thin walls. These thin walls mean that substances can easily **diffuse** into and out of the blood.

2 a What does excrete mean?
  b What substance do the lungs excrete?

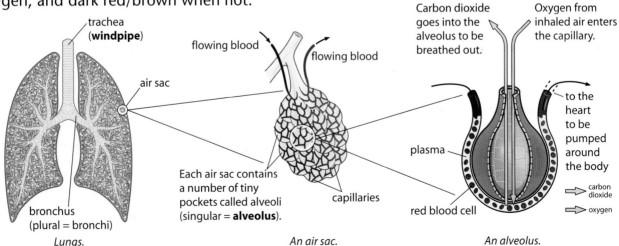

trachea (**windpipe**)

air sac

bronchus (plural = bronchi)

Lungs.

flowing blood

flowing blood

Each air sac contains a number of tiny pockets called alveoli (singular = **alveolus**).

capillaries

An air sac.

Carbon dioxide goes into the alveolus to be breathed out.

Oxygen from inhaled air enters the capillary.

to the heart to be pumped around the body

plasma

red blood cell

carbon dioxide

oxygen

An alveolus.

C

3 a What is gas exchange?
   b Where in the lungs does gas exchange occur?
   c List three ways in which the lungs are adapted for gas exchange.

4 How are each of these substances carried by the blood?
   a oxygen   b carbon dioxide
   (*Hint*: You may need to look back at page 25 and 28).

5 Your veins are not blue, although they look that way through the skin.
   a What colour is the blood in an artery?
   b What colour is it in a vein?
   c New babies sometimes look blue, when *all* their blood vessels look the same colour as veins through the skin. What might cause this?   Ⓗ Ⓢ Ⓦ

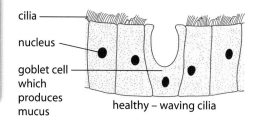

You have about 300 million alveoli, which give your lungs a huge surface area – about the size of a tennis court!

cilia

nucleus

goblet cell which produces mucus

healthy – waving cilia

unhealthy – 'lifeless' cilia

Ⓓ

Reduced gas exchange

Cells in the tubes leading down to the lungs make a sticky liquid called **mucus**. This traps dust, dirt and germs. **Cilia** are found on **ciliated epithelial cells** in the **trachea** and **bronchi**. These tiny hairs sweep mucus out of the lungs and into the gullet where it is swallowed. This is how the lungs are kept clean.

The chemicals and heat in cigarette smoke stop cilia working. The mucus then collects in the lungs and reduces the surface area for gas exchange.

Smoke also irritates the alveoli. With time this causes the alveoli to break down (a condition called emphysema) which again reduces the surface area. Breathing in large amounts of dust over a long period causes similar problems.

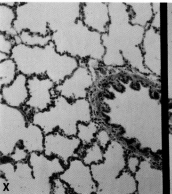
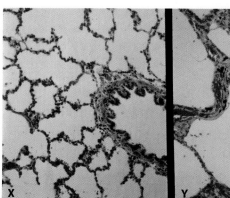

X   Y

Ⓔ *Very thin slices from two lungs. One is from someone with emphysema.*

6 Cigarette smoke contains carbon monoxide. Why are the oxygen levels in a smoker's blood less than those in a non-smoker? Give as many reasons as you can.   Ⓗ Ⓢ Ⓦ

7 A doctor examines the microscope slides in E.   Ⓗ Ⓢ Ⓦ
   a Which slide is from someone with emphysema? Explain your reasoning.
   b Predict whether that person would have a higher or lower breathing rate than someone who does not have the disease. Explain your reasoning.

8 Does information on lung diseases help people make choices about smoking? Explain your reasoning.   Ⓗ Ⓢ Ⓦ

I CAN...

o describe how the respiratory system allows gas exchange.
o consider how a knowledge of science informs personal decisions.   H S Ⓦ

How are inhaled and exhaled air different?

The air we breathe out is called **exhaled air**. It is different to **inhaled air**.

1 What is inhaled air?
2 Look at the picture of the two gas jars. (H)(S)(W)
   a Which gas jar do you think contains exhaled air?
   b Explain your answer.

Table B shows the differences between inhaled and exhaled air. Some of these differences are due to respiration, which happens in all your cells.

(H)(S)(W)

How could you find out if the amount of oxygen you exhale changes when you exercise?

Athletes want to absorb as much oxygen from the air as possible. This is measured using equipment like that shown in photo C, which provides valuable information for trainers.

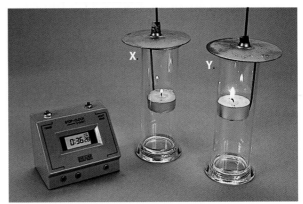

A One of these candles is in exhaled air.

	Inhaled air	Exhaled air
nitrogen gas	78%	78%
oxygen gas	21%	16%
carbon dioxide gas	0.03%	4%
water vapour	variable	more
temperature	variable	warmer
dirt particles	variable	cleaner

B Differences between inhaled and exhaled air.

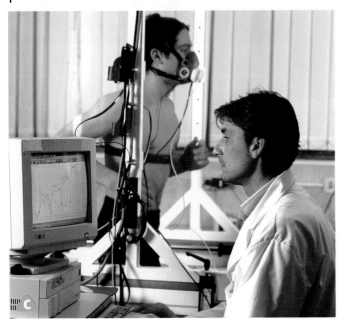

3 The amount of nitrogen in inhaled air is the same as that in exhaled air. Suggest a reason for this.
4 Why is there less oxygen in exhaled air than inhaled air?
5 Why is there more carbon dioxide in exhaled air than inhaled air?
6 Exhaled air is warmer than inhaled air. Explain why.
7 Inhaled air is dirtier than exhaled air. Explain why.
8 a Display the information comparing inhaled and exhaled air as two pie charts. (H)(S)(W)
   b What are the advantages of showing this data as a pie chart? (H)(S)(W)
   c What are the disadvantages? (H)(S)(W)

Organisms that live in water also need oxygen for respiration. The oxygen is dissolved in the water. Plants that grow underwater get their oxygen by diffusion. Oxygen diffuses into the cells from the surrounding water.

A fish gets oxygen by taking in water through its mouth and forcing it over its **gills**. The gills have a large surface area and a good blood supply so that oxygen can quickly diffuse from the water into the blood.

Oxygen diffuses into the leaves from the water.

Water flows in through the fish's mouth.

In the gills the oxygen diffuses from the water into the blood.

D *Gas exchange in pondweed and fish.*

> 9 Gills are adapted to absorb lots of oxygen. Explain how.
> 10 How do you think fish excrete carbon dioxide?

Power stations use a lot of water for cooling. They take it from rivers and return the warmed water to the rivers. However, less oxygen dissolves in warmer water. Fish can die in warm water because they can't get enough oxygen.

New power stations try to stop this happening. The Barking Power Station in Essex monitors the temperature of the river Thames. If the water temperature near the power station reaches 21.5 °C, a standby cooling system is used instead of river water.

E *Barking Power Station.*

H S W

In water containing a normal amount of carbon dioxide, **hydrogencarbonate indicator** is pink.
Adding more carbon dioxide turns it yellow. Removing carbon dioxide turns it purple.

o How would you show that fish carry out respiration?

> 11 What can happen to fish if warm water is released into rivers?
> 12 a What colour would hydrogencarbonate indicator solution turn if you breathed into it through a straw?   H S W
>   b Explain why it would turn this colour.
> 13 In what way is Barking Power Station an example of sustainable development?   H S W

I CAN...

o explain the differences between inhaled and exhaled air.
o recall how gas exchange occurs in some water organisms.
o use hydrogencarbonate indicator to test for carbon dioxide.   H S W

Some athletes cheat. Their **behaviour** can be caused by an intense pressure from those around them to win events. It can, however, be difficult to draw the line between what is cheating and what is not.

Drugs

In 1964 Finnish cross-country skier Eero Mäntyranta won two Olympic gold medals. He could ski harder than his rivals because he had more red blood cells than the others. His body naturally produced more of a chemical, nicknamed 'epo', which causes red blood cell production. In 1989 a drugs company started selling artificial epo to help people with AIDS. The drug was soon being used by athletes.

Some athletes take steroids (drugs that increase muscle growth). Testosterone is a steroid made in your body. Some people naturally produce more than others.

Gene therapy

Blood is regularly taken from athletes to test for artificial drugs but some athletes are trying gene therapy. Athletes are injecting themselves with material that causes their cells to start naturally producing more testosterone or epo. This is difficult to detect.

Devices

South African Oscar Pistorius lost his legs as a baby. He runs using springy 'blades'. He wanted to compete in the Olympics but was told that his blades gave him an advantage and was not allowed to take part. Eventually this decision was overturned and he was allowed to compete.

HAVE YOUR SAY

Was it right to allow Oscar Pistorius to compete in the Olympics, or should he only have been allowed to compete in the Paralympics?

HowScienceWorks

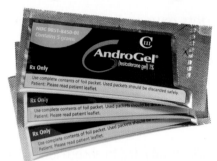

A Some athletes abuse steroids like this.

Oscar Pistorius **B** *competing in a 400m race in Rome (against able-bodied athletes) where he came second.*

1 a Explain why having more red blood cells helped Eero Mäntyranta.
  b This is an example of **inherited variation**. What **environmental factor** could cause the same effect?

2 What are the drawbacks of developing new steroids to help people suffering from diseases?

3 Medical scientists could collaborate with the people responsible for testing athletes. New drugs could be made with harmless 'markers', which would show up easily in someone's blood. What effects would this idea have on:
  a companies that develop the drugs
  b patients that use the drugs in hospitals
  c athletes who wish to use drugs like this?

4 On balance, do you think using 'markers' is a good idea? Explain your reasoning.

How**S**cience**W**orks

Some people catch diseases in hospitals. Many of these diseases are caused by 'superbugs', so-called because they are very difficult to treat. Two common ones are MRSA and *C. difficile*.

Hospital bosses could face charges after outbreak kills 90

MANSLAUGHTER BY SUPERBUG?

A

1 Why is collecting data from hospitals useful?

The government collects a lot of **data** from hospitals. At the beginning of this century the government saw that MRSA was becoming a big problem. Scientists knew that more people got MRSA in dirty hospitals. So the government introduced strict rules on cleaning and frequent inspections of hospital cleaning.

2 a Look at graph B. In which year do you think the new cleaning rules were introduced? Explain your reasoning.

  b In 2007 a government minister said: 'We have already had a lot of success in reducing the incidence of MRSA'. Was the minister right?

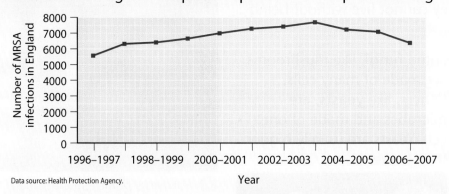

Data source: Health Protection Agency.

B *Number of patients in England found with MRSA in their blood.*

Franziska Hammerschmidt is a microbiologist at Heartlands Hospital, Birmingham. As part of her job she keeps a check on how clean things are in the hospital. If she does not think that something is clean enough she reports it so that it can be cleaned quickly.

C *Franziska Hammerschmidt.*

3 Look at chart D.
  a What does the bar chart tell you?
  b If you were a government minister, would you put graph B or chart D into a report about MRSA? Explain your answer.

4 a Why is MRSA called a 'superbug'?
  b Who do you think invented the term 'superbug' – scientists or newspapers? Explain your reasoning.
  c Do you think 'superbug' is a good term to use?

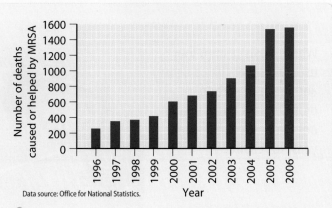

Data source: Office for National Statistics.

D *Deaths caused or helped by MRSA in England.*

What are microbes?

An **organism** is a living thing. All organisms carry out seven life processes: movement, reproduction, sensitivity, growth, respiration, excretion, nutrition. MRSA is an example of a **microbe** or **micro-organism** – an organism that you need a microscope to see. Most microbes are made of only one cell.

Viruses are the smallest microbes. They are very difficult to see even with the most powerful microscopes. The largest are only about 0.000 000 3 mm wide! Most scientists do not think of them as organisms because they cannot live without being inside living cells.

Bacteria are much bigger than viruses and are definitely living things. The singular of bacteria is **bacterium**.

Some **fungi**, like mushrooms, are made of many cells. Others, like **yeasts**, are microbes and made of one cell. Yeasts are usually bigger than bacteria.

1 Which life processes do these phrases refer to?
 a detecting things around them
 b getting rid of the waste that they make
 c using food.

2 Use the first letters of the seven life processes to create a silly word or phrase to help you remember them (a mnemonic).

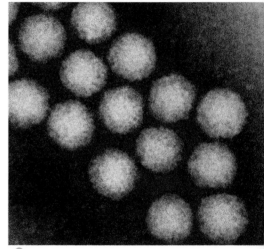

A *Poliovirus particles (magnified × 385 000).*

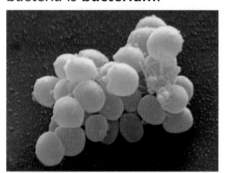

B *MRSA bacteria (magnified × 8300).*

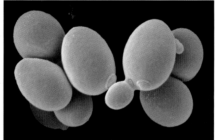

C *Yeast cells (magnified × 8300).*

3 List two things that viruses cannot do that living things can.

4 What sort of microbe is MRSA?

5 Draw a table to compare the three different types of microbes. **H S W**

When yeasts respire they use up a sugar (like glucose) and produce carbon dioxide. How might you find out the best conditions for yeast to respire?

H S W

yeast cells in a growing solution

glucose

D water

I CAN...

- recall the seven life processes.
- describe the differences between the three types of microbe.

How are microbes different?

As microscopes have become more and more powerful, cells have been studied in more detail. We now classify organisms into one of five **kingdoms** based on what their cells look like.

Cell part	*all other than P, f- f?* Kingdom				
	Bacteria	**Protoctists**	**Fungi**	**Plants**	**Animals**
Nucleus	✗	✓	✓	✓	✓
Cell wall	✓ soft and made of glycoprotein	✓ different types in different species	✓ mainly made of chitin	✓ mainly made of cellulose	✗
Chloroplasts	✗	found in some species	✗	✓	✗

A

Viruses are made of a **protein coat** that contains a **strand of genes**. The genes contain the instructions for making new viruses. When a virus gets into a cell, these genes cause the cell to make new copies of the virus. This is known as **replication**.

3 What is a virus made of?
4 a What is virus replication?
   b Why do you think it is not called 'reproduction'?

Bacteria are single cells that do not contain a nucleus. Their genes are found on a circular **chromosome**. On the outside of a bacterium is a soft cell wall. Some bacteria have 'tails' called **flagellae**, which help them to move.

Like all fungi, all yeast cells have a nucleus that contains chromosomes. They also have vacuoles to store substances in.

5 a List one thing that an animal cell has but a bacterium does not.
   b List two things that both animal cells and bacteria have.
6 List two differences between bacteria and yeasts.
7 Organisms used to be **classified** by the way they looked on the outside. **H S W**
   a Why is it better to look at the insides of their cells?
   b The development of what has allowed us to do this?

1 Which kingdoms contain organisms that can make their own food? Explain how you know.
2 Why is there not a kingdom for viruses?

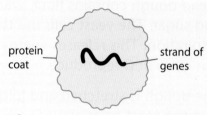

B Viruses have simple structures.

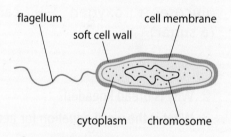

C Bacteria are living cells.

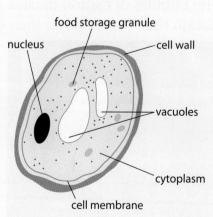

D Yeast cells are more complex than bacterial cells.

How are microbes useful?

Some microbes are used to make certain foods and drinks. For example, some yeasts are very important in baking and brewing.

> **1** List three foods or drinks that are made with the help of yeast.

| made using microbes that are fungi | made using bacteria and fungi | made using bacteria |

A Some foods made using microbes.

Baking

Bread dough contains flour, water, yeast cells and sugar. The yeast cells use the sugar for respiration. This releases energy so that they can grow and reproduce.

The dough is stretched and folded (kneaded) to trap air in it so that the yeast have enough oxygen for **aerobic respiration**.

> **glucose** + **oxygen** → **carbon dioxide** + **water**
> (a sugar)

> **2** Why is bread kneaded?
> **3** What is the word equation for aerobic respiration?

The bubbles of carbon dioxide gas from respiration make the dough rise. The dough is then baked in an oven.

B Bread dough being kneaded.

C Bread dough rising.

D UK bakers Warburtons produce over two million loaves of bread every day.

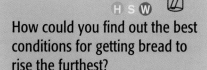

H S W

How could you find out the best conditions for getting bread to rise the furthest?

water

E

H S W !

Usually when making wine, the carbon dioxide escapes. However, if champagne is being made, the carbon dioxide is kept in the wine to give it its fizz.

Brewing

Beer and wine are also made using yeast. However, in brewing air is kept *out* of the mixture. When there is no oxygen, yeasts use **anaerobic respiration**, and in yeasts this process produces ethanol (alcohol). When yeasts respire anaerobically it is known as **fermentation**. If barley grains are fermented, beer is made, whereas grapes are used to make wine.

glucose → carbon dioxide + ethanol
(a sugar)

4 a What is anaerobic respiration?
   b What is it called when yeasts respire anaerobically?

The juice to be fermented has a small amount of a solution containing growing yeast cells added to it. This is called a **starter culture**. The yeast cells continue to grow and reproduce. They reproduce by **budding** in which a new cell grows out of a 'parent' cell. The new cell grows in size and then it too can produce a 'bud cell'. You can see this in photo C on page 36.

In the right conditions (warmth, moisture and plenty of sugar) microbes like yeasts reproduce very quickly. A few cells soon become millions. However, the **population** of cells will not keep growing forever. Eventually the sugar runs out and the population stops growing. Something that slows down or stops a population growing is called a **limiting factor**.

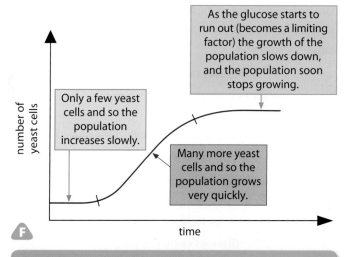

As the glucose starts to run out (becomes a limiting factor) the growth of the population slows down, and the population soon stops growing.

Only a few yeast cells and so the population increases slowly.

Many more yeast cells and so the population grows very quickly.

number of yeast cells

time

F

5 What is a 'population'?

6 Some yeast cells are added to a beaker of glucose solution. The number of yeast cells increases for 8 hours and then stops increasing.   H S W
  a Why does the number of cells increase?
  b Why does the population stop increasing?

7 If bread dough is made so that it contains hardly any air, the dough still rises a bit. What process happens to allow the bread to rise?

8 Draw diagrams to show how one yeast cell becomes three.   H S W

I CAN...

o describe how microbes help in the production of some foods and drinks.

o describe the differences between aerobic and anaerobic respiration.

o interpret a graph of population size using a knowledge of limiting factors.   H S W

8Cc Under attack

How do microbes spread and cause diseases?

Microbes are all around us. Most are harmless but some have unpleasant effects, like making food go bad or milk go sour. Some microbes cause **diseases**.

The effects of a disease are called **symptoms**. A doctor observes symptoms and uses them to come up with a **diagnosis** (an idea about what has caused those symptoms).

> 1 'Colds' are caused by viruses. Write down two symptoms of having a cold.

Diseases caused by viruses	
Symptoms	**Diagnosis**
fever, raised red spots with yellow tops found on face and chest (more on chest)	chickenpox
fever, red eyes, flat red spots on face and chest (more on the face)	measles
high temperature (fever), sore throat, muscles ache	flu (short for influenza)
Diseases caused by bacteria	
blisters cover the face and chest, leaving yellow scabs	impetigo
vomiting, stomach pain, diarrhoea	food poisoning
a pale red rash covers the whole body	syphilis
very watery diarrhoea, vomiting, muscle cramps	cholera
fever, tiredness, coughing up blood	tuberculosis (TB)
Diseases caused by fungi	
skin between the toes is red, itchy and peeling	athlete's foot
white patches in the mouth or vagina	thrush (caused by a yeast)

B

> 2 Name one disease caused by:
>   a a fungus   b a virus   c a bacterium.
> 3 How would a doctor diagnose food poisoning? Ⓗ Ⓢ Ⓦ
> 4 Many diseases cause a **fever**. What is a fever?

Bacteria in your armpits cause body odour. Photo A shows an experiment to try to find out which deodorant works best!

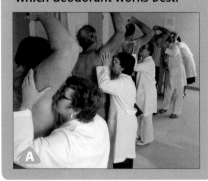

A

Diseases that can be spread from person to person (or from animal to person) are **infectious**.

Air

When someone coughs or sneezes, a spray of tiny watery droplets enters the air. These may contain microbes. If someone else breathes in the droplets they may become infected by the microbes and get a disease. Colds, flu, chickenpox, measles and TB are all spread in this way.

C *Special photography can show the droplets in a sneeze. These droplets can travel at up to 100 km/h!*

5 What is an infectious disease?

6 Name a disease spread through the air, caused by
  a a virus   b a bacterium.

Touch

Some diseases are passed on by touching an infected person (e.g. impetigo). Athlete's foot can be spread by touch or indirectly, by treading barefoot on a wet floor where an infected person has recently trodden. MRSA can be spread from person to person by touch or by contact with sheets, clothing or equipment.

Water

In overcrowded conditions, like refugee camps, people's **sewage** can get into the drinking water. This is how the bacterium that causes cholera spreads.

Food

Food poisoning is caused by bacteria in food. Animals learn to avoid eating certain foods that make them ill. Humans have learned to cook food. Cooking food thoroughly kills bacteria.

Animals

Some microbes are carried by animals. For example, mosquitoes carry the microbes that cause malaria and yellow fever.

Sex

Some diseases are passed on when people have sex (e.g. syphilis).

9 Why is learning not to eat certain foods useful to an animal?

10 Imagine you are a doctor. These people come to see you. Ⓗ Ⓢ Ⓦ

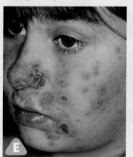
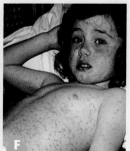
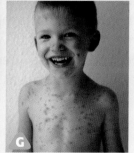

  a What diagnosis would you make for each patient?
  b Suggest how each person may have got their disease.

7 Why do you think cholera often occurs in areas hit by wars or natural disasters?

8 A hospital has a problem with MRSA. Suggest some measures they could take to stop its spread. Ⓗ Ⓢ Ⓦ

H S Ⓦ

Christopher Columbus reached the Caribbean islands in 1492. There is a **theory** that his sailors infected the local people with measles and smallpox, killing many of them. There is also a theory that the sailors brought syphilis back with them.

I CAN...

o recall a disease caused by each different sort of microbe.

o apply knowledge of the ways in which microbes are spread to avoid getting diseases. H S Ⓦ

How did John Snow work out how cholera was spread?

Dr William Farr (1807–1883) thought that cholera was caused by 'bad air'. Dr John Snow (1813–1858) did not believe this theory.

Snow made careful observations of where and how infected people lived. He found that people who stayed healthy often used a different water supply from their neighbours who caught cholera. This led Snow to think that cholera was spread in the water.

> 1 Why do you think Snow did not believe Farr's theory?
> 2 What was Snow's theory?

HowScienceWorks

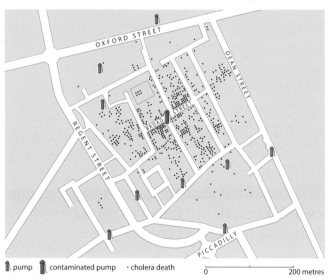

🚰 pump   🚰 contaminated pump   · cholera death   0   200 metres

A *Each spot represents a death.*

In 1854 nearly 500 people died in 10 days around Broad Street in London. The people in this area got water from pumps in the streets. Snow marked the deaths on a map and drew in the positions of the pumps (diagram A).

Looking at his map, Snow predicted that if the Broad Street pump was closed, people would stop getting cholera. He decided to get the pump handle removed. Soon afterwards people stopped getting cholera. This provided more evidence for his theory. Farr still didn't believe Snow and carried on collecting data to support his own theory. However, Farr let Snow have all the data he collected.

By 1866 Farr had come to accept Snow's theory. There was another outbreak of cholera and Farr observed that people who took water from the Old Ford reservoir in East London were most likely to get the disease. This provided more evidence that Snow was right. The bacterium that causes cholera was finally discovered in 1883.

B *A replica pump in Broadwick Street (formerly Broad Street). Notice that it has no handle.*

> 3 a What is a theory?
>   b How did Snow's map provide evidence to support his theory?
> 4 In what way did Farr and Snow collaborate?

I CAN...

o describe how evidence supports a theory.

8Cd Stopping the spread

How do we stop diseases spreading?

In the middle of the nineteenth century, cities smelled disgusting. Sewage was often stored in cellars (cesspits) under houses or flowed into the streets where it collected in small ditches in the road. The sewage often leaked into the water supply.

Diseases were very common; poor workmen in London often died before reaching the age of 20! After it was discovered that sewage in drinking water caused diseases, sewer tunnels were built and water was used to wash the sewage away. This greatly reduced the number of people with diseases.

Proper sewage disposal was the most important development in stopping people dying from diseases. Today, we also try to kill microbes or stop them growing. This is particularly important in hospitals.

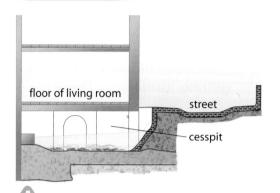

floor of living room   street
cesspit

A

Method	Used to ...	Prevents the spread of ...
pasteurisation	pasteurise milk (heated to 70 °C for 15 seconds to kill harmful bacteria)	tuberculosis
disinfectants	kill bacteria in toilets and around buildings	stomach upsets, legionnaire's disease
soaps and **antiseptics** (in toothpastes and deodorants)	kill bacteria on our bodies	skin diseases, stomach upsets
chlorine in drinking water	kill bacteria in water	cholera, typhoid, stomach upsets
salting, canning, pickling in vinegar	kill microbes in foods	stomach upsets
drying, freezing, refrigeration	stop or slow the growth of microbes in food	stomach upsets
cooking foods well	kill off bacteria	food poisoning

B

1 Why do you think building sewers reduced the number of people with diseases? **H S W**

2 Make a list of all the ways in which bacteria have been stopped from getting to you today. **H S W**

3 Which methods in table B do you think hospitals use to stop the spread of MRSA? **H S W**

4 It is against the law to sell unpasteurised milk in supermarkets. What do you think of this law? **H S W**

!

A sewer tunnel designed in 1858 by Isambard Kingdom Brunel was built under the Thames. Queen Victoria liked it so much that she asked for a railway to be put in it. It never became a sewer and today it is part of the Bakerloo Underground line!

H S W

How could you find out if washing with soap helps to remove bacteria? Or is plain water just as good?

C

I CAN...

o describe some ways in which we control microbes.

43

8Cd Self-defence

How does your body protect you against diseases?

Your body has ways of killing microbes and stopping them getting inside you. These are your **natural defences**.

A chemical in your tears kills bacteria.

Hairs in your nose trap some microbes.

Acid in your stomach kills microbes.

Skin helps to keep microbes out of the body; if you cut yourself, a **clot** (called a **scab**) forms and this stops microbes getting in.

Cells in your **trachea** (windpipe) and nose produce sticky mucus, which traps microbes. **Ciliated epithelial cells** sweep the mucus to the top of your gullet to be swallowed.

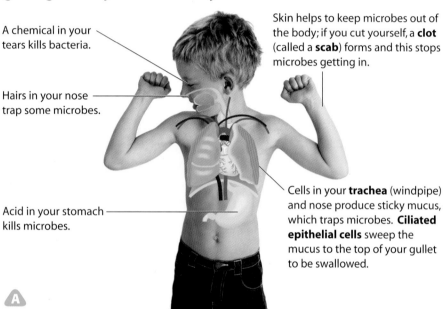

A

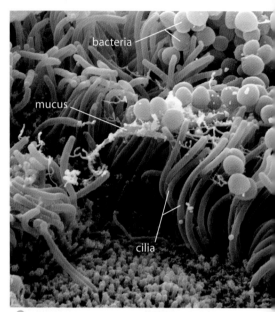

B *Magnification × 8 300.*

White blood cells destroy microbes. Some of them **engulf** (surround and digest) microbes.

Other white blood cells make **antibodies**. These stick to microbes, making it easier for them to be engulfed. Antibodies can also make the microbes stick together or burst open. However, antibodies have to be specially made by your body to attach to each different sort of microbe and this takes time.

The white blood cells of babies are not as good at fighting microbes as those of older children. Breastfeeding can help since breast milk contains antibodies.

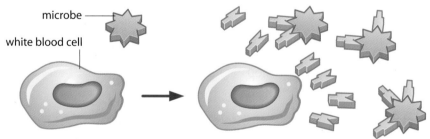

microbe

white blood cell

The white blood cell finds a microbe and starts to make antibodies.

The antibodies are made specially to fit onto the outside of the microbe. Each type of microbe has a different surface and so needs a different type of antibody.

C

1 Why is it important to form a scab quickly?

2 a What is mucus?
  b What does it do?
  c Name two places where it is produced.

3 a List three things antibodies can do to microbes.
  b Why does it take time for antibodies to be produced?

4 Antibodies are said to be 'specific' for a certain microbe. What does this mean?

I CAN...

o describe the body's natural defences used to protect it from microbes.

How is AIDS spread and how is it treated?

AIDS (Acquired Immune Deficiency Syndrome) is caused by the Human Immunodeficiency Virus (**HIV**).

The virus has killed more than 25 million people since it was first discovered in 1981. Few people die of AIDS in the UK. Millions die of it in Africa. There is still no cure.

HIV infects **T4 lymphocytes** – white blood cells that are vital for destroying microbes. The strand of genes from the virus is inserted into the cell's DNA. This causes the cells to **replicate** the virus. The new viruses then burst out of the cell, destroying it. Over many years the virus destroys more and more T4 lymphocytes. When there are very few left, the body cannot defend itself from microbes and the person has AIDS.

HIV is spread when the blood of an infected (**HIV positive**) person mixes with the blood of an uninfected person, usually through sex and by drug addicts sharing needles. It cannot be passed on by normal contact with an HIV-positive person.

Drugs can keep the virus under control but these are expensive and cannot be afforded by poor countries, especially in Africa where AIDS is a big problem. This is not helped by some people denying the link between HIV and AIDS, despite a lot of evidence. In 2006, the South African health minister told HIV-positive people to eat garlic and beetroot to cure themselves.

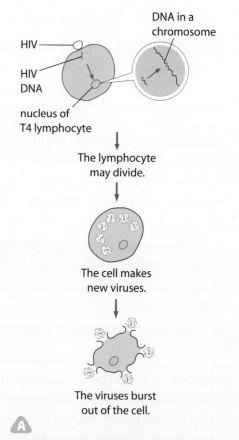

HIV
HIV DNA
nucleus of T4 lymphocyte
DNA in a chromosome

The lymphocyte may divide.

The cell makes new viruses.

The viruses burst out of the cell.

A

1 Explain how millions of T4 lymphocytes get infected with the virus if only one gets into the body.

2 Why might a person with AIDS die from a disease caused by a bacterium?

3 Why do more people die of AIDS in Africa than in the UK? Give as many possible reasons as you can. Ⓗ Ⓢ Ⓦ

4 Describe one piece of evidence that you think scientists have to support the theory that HIV causes AIDS. Ⓗ Ⓢ Ⓦ

5 UNAIDS is a collaboration of people who aim to educate people about AIDS, monitor the spread of AIDS and try to provide cheaper medicines to poorer countries. Write a list of people who need to collaborate to achieve these aims. Ⓗ Ⓢ Ⓦ

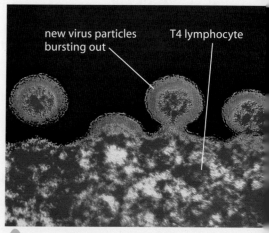

new virus particles bursting out
T4 lymphocyte

B *Magnification ×100 000.*

How do you become immune to diseases?

If you get infected with microbes, they reproduce. It takes time for your body to make antibodies and so you get the disease until there are enough antibodies to destroy all the microbes.

After having a disease, some antibodies stay in your blood, often forever. So, your body remains ready for that particular microbe if it infects you again. You will not get that disease again – you are **immune**.

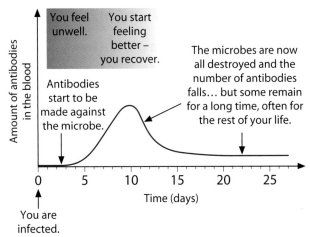

A

1 What does it mean if you are immune to a disease?

A **vaccine** can also make you immune to a disease and is often given in an injection. When you are made immune it is called **immunisation**.

A vaccine contains microbes that have been treated to stop them causing their disease. Your body produces antibodies against the treated microbes. Many of these antibodies stay in your blood ready to help destroy the real microbes quickly if you are infected by them. Antibodies can pass from a mother to her baby through the placenta and breast milk. This helps babies to fight infections.

Age of person	Vaccine given
2–4 months	diphtheria, whooping cough, polio, tetanus, bacterial meningitis
1–2 years	measles, mumps, rubella
3–5 years	diphtheria, tetanus, polio
10–14 years (girls only)	rubella (if not immunised earlier)
13 years	tuberculosis (TB)
16–19 years	tetanus, polio
Adults	tetanus every 5–10 years

B *Normal ages for immunisations in the UK. Some immunisations are given more than once so that the body builds up a high level of antibodies. The extra injections are called 'boosters'.*

Edward Jenner (1749–1823) invented vaccines. He gave people a mild disease called cowpox to stop them getting smallpox (a very nasty disease). Thanks to immunisation smallpox no longer exists. The last case was in Africa in 1978.

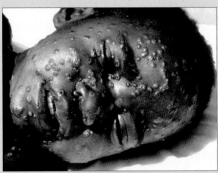

C *A child with smallpox.*

2 Sketch a graph to show the changes in the number of antibodies after an immunisation. H S W

3 Chickenpox and measles are caused by viruses.
   a Why do you usually only get chickenpox once?
   b If you have had chickenpox can you still get measles? Explain your answer.
   c How can you make sure you never get measles?

I CAN...

o explain why immunisations are given.

How do antibiotics work?

Vaccines cannot be made for every disease but **medicines** can treat and cure many diseases.

Antibiotics harm bacteria. They were discovered in 1928 by Alexander Fleming (1881–1955). Fleming noticed mould growing in a dish he was using to grow bacteria. He observed that the bacteria did not grow near the mould.

Fleming came up with a theory that the mould produced a chemical that harmed the bacteria. He was right. Howard Florey (1898–1968) and Ernst Chain (1906–1979) purified the substance and made the first antibiotic medicine – penicillin.

Different antibiotics harm different bacteria. Some antibiotics are made by chemically altering penicillin to make it kill different bacteria. One of these antibiotics is methicillin. Bacteria that are not harmed by an antibiotic are **resistant**. MRSA stands for methicillin-resistant *Staphylococcus aureus*. Scientists are trying to develop new antibiotics to kill this bacterium.

Antibiotics do not work on viruses. Other medicines are used to ease the symptoms of viral diseases (e.g. aspirin reduces your temperature).

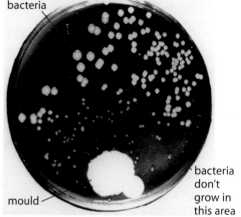

bacteria

mould — bacteria don't grow in this area

A One of Fleming's dishes.

1 What are antibiotics?
2 a What theory did Fleming come up with?
  b What evidence supported this theory?

Soaking paper discs in antibiotics and putting the discs on agar covered with bacteria will test the antibiotics.
o How would you test three antibiotics against the *E. coli* bacterium?
o How would you tell which was the best antibiotic?

!

2500 years ago the Chinese put mouldy bean curd on skin infections. They were using an antibiotic!

B *Prof. Brian Austin is developing an antibiotic from bacteria that grow on seaweed. His results suggest that it can kill MRSA.*

3 What does it mean if a bacterium is resistant to an antibiotic?
4 Why can't colds be cured by antibiotics?
5 a Why is scientific research like Prof. Austin's important?
  b Suggest what needs to be done before his antibiotic can be used.

I CAN...
o describe how antibiotics are used.

8Ce Medical problems

How useful are antibiotics?

Some scientists think that using antibiotics and vaccines against some bacterial diseases, like tuberculosis (TB), has made little difference.

> **1** How does graph A support the theory that antibiotics have made no difference?

Many scientists think that the overuse of antibiotics has caused problems, including the 'superbug' problem. The number of people getting TB is now rising again, and the bacterium is now resistant to many antibiotics.

In any population of bacteria, there is **variation** and some bacteria may be naturally resistant to an antibiotic. This is of benefit to the survival of the bacteria. The antibiotic will not kill resistant bacteria, which can then spread to other people and cause infections that cannot now be treated with the antibiotic. Bacteria can also pick up the material that makes them resistant from other bacteria.

> **2 a** In photo B, which antibiotics is the bacterium resistant to?
> **b** What might the results look like if MRSA bacteria were used?

Penicillin used to be used to treat many infections. Now it is useless against many bacteria because they have become resistant.

Antibiotics kill bacteria in your intestines. Some of these are good bacteria and keep the numbers of bad bacteria down. Killing the good bacteria leaves the bad bacteria to reproduce. For instance, many people have a type of bacteria called *C. difficile* inside them. Without good bacteria to keep it under control, it can cause a severe intestine disease that can only be treated with powerful antibiotics.

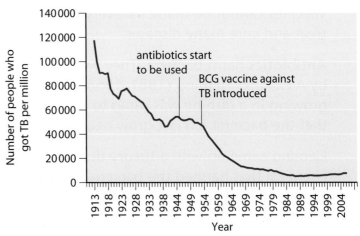

Data source: Health Protection Agency Centre for Infections.

A *Cases of TB in England and Wales. Some scientists think that air pollution helps the bacterium to cause TB.*

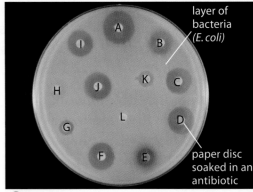

layer of bacteria (*E. coli*)

paper disc soaked in an antibiotic

B *Some antibiotics are better at killing a type of bacterium than others.*

> **3** Some farm animals are given antibiotics in their food all the time.
> **a** Why do you think a farmer would do this?
> **b** What problems might this cause?

HAVE YOUR SAY

Antibiotics should only be given out by hospitals. What do you think of this idea?

Dead as a dodo

HowScienceworks

Sailors discovered dodo birds on the island of Mauritius in about 1507. The birds were not afraid of people. Less than 200 years later they were **extinct**.

No one knows what dodos looked like! Most evidence comes from paintings. The model in photo A is based on a painting. Some museums have skeletons but these are made of bones from many dodos. The only known stuffed dodo rotted in the Oxford Museum of Natural History and so was burned in 1775! However, we think of dodos as being fat and clumsy.

In 1990 Dr Andrew Kitchener (from the National Museum of Scotland) looked through images of dodos and spotted a trend. Images from before about 1605 showed thin birds, and those after about 1625 showed fat birds. He developed a theory that the later paintings were of overfed captive birds. He said that wild dodos would have been thin and active creatures.

A Dodo model with stuck on swan feathers!

1 Suggest why dodos became extinct. Think of as many possible reasons as you can.

2 Why don't museum skeletons of dodos provide good evidence for what they looked like?

B Dodo drawing from an engraving by Carl Clusius in 1605.

C Dodo painting by Hans I Savery from 1651.

In 1991 some new drawings of dodos from 1601 were discovered in Holland (photo D).

Today, geologists and biologists are working together in a swamp in Mauritius looking for dodo bones and **fossils**. They are hoping to find a complete skeleton.

3 Does photo D provide evidence for or against Kitchener's theory?
4 Why do different scientists work together?

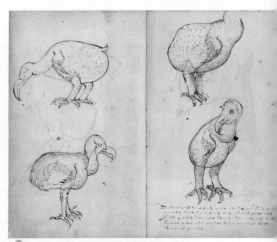

D Dodo drawings made by a ship's captain in 1601.

8Da Death of the dinosaurs

Why did the dinosaurs become extinct?

Dinosaurs appeared on Earth about 230 million years ago. They became extinct about 65 million years ago. There are over 100 theories about why this happened!

Organisms are **adapted** to their **habitats**. **Physical environmental factors**, like temperature, help to create the **environment** of a habitat. If an environment changes, the organisms may not be adapted to the new environment and so may die out.

Volcanoes

Huge volcanic eruptions occurred in India 65 million years ago. Some scientists think that these put billions of tonnes of sulphur dioxide and carbon dioxide into the air, causing **acid rain** and **global warming**. It got too hot for dinosaurs. The rocks formed by these huge eruptions can be seen across much of India today.

> **3** What evidence supports the theory that volcanoes caused dinosaur extinction?

Meteorite impact

Some scientists think that a giant meteorite hit the Earth, throwing vast quantities of rock and earth into the atmosphere, blocking out sunlight and making it very cold. The cold killed off the dinosaurs. The remains of a 180 km-wide crater caused by an impact 65 million years ago have been found near Mexico.

> **4** What evidence supports the theory that a meteorite caused dinosaur extinction?

HowScienceWorks

A *A model dinosaur – an* Ankylosaurus.

> **1** Give one way in which you think an *Ankylosaurus* was adapted to its habitat.
>
> **2 a** List one adaptation a polar bear has for surviving in cold environments.
>
> **b** Why might polar bears become extinct if their habitat becomes warm?

B *The Barringer Crater in the USA is much smaller than the one near Mexico. It is only 1.2 km wide and was formed 50 000 years ago.*

Disease

Another idea is that a disease killed the dinosaurs. This theory has less 'weight' than other theories because it does not explain all the evidence. For example, it does not explain why so many sea animals died at the same time.

Finding evidence

Organisms in the **animal kingdom** are **classified** into groups.

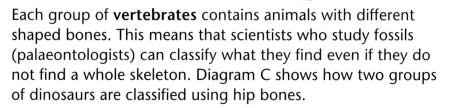

animal kingdom

vertebrates

mammals (hair)   **reptiles** (dry scales)   **fish** (slimy wet scales)   **amphibians** (moist skin)   **birds** (feathers)

crocodiles   **dinosaurs**

Saurischia   **Ornithischia**

There are three 'hip' bones and the lower front one points forwards.

The lower front hip bone becomes thin and points backwards.

C

invertebrates

5 Another theory to explain dinosaur extinction is that small mammals ate many dinosaur eggs. This theory does not carry as much weight as the meteorite theory. Why not?

Each group of **vertebrates** contains animals with different shaped bones. This means that scientists who study fossils (palaeontologists) can classify what they find even if they do not find a whole skeleton. Diagram C shows how two groups of dinosaurs are classified using hip bones.

Scientists find other evidence in rocks too. All over the world there is a band of rock from 65 million years ago that contains a lot of a very rare metal called iridium. It is found in liquid rocks deep inside the Earth and also in asteroids.

D Fossilised dinosaur bones.

6 In photo D, the scientist is uncovering a dinosaur hip bone. What group of dinosaurs does the bone belong to? Explain your reasoning.

7 a List four theories to explain how dinosaurs became extinct.
   b Which theory or theories does the band of iridium support?
   c Explain how this band could have got where it is.

I CAN...

- explain why changes in an environment can cause organisms to die.
- recall how animals are classified.
- explain why some theories carry more 'weight' than others.

What evidence do plant fossils provide?

Many members of the **plant kingdom** also became extinct 65 million years ago.

It is very difficult to tell what many of these plants looked like, but whole fossil trees can sometimes be found.

B A 270 million-year-old fossilised pine tree in Africa.

This layer of pale rock is 65 million years old and contains a lot of a rare metal called iridium.

This leaf is only found in rocks older than 65 million years old.

A

1 What is the evidence that many plants died out 65 million years ago? Ⓗ Ⓢ Ⓦ

2 Why can't we tell exactly what many of these plants looked like? Ⓗ Ⓢ Ⓦ

Evidence from plants

Fossilised plants can tell us what an environment was like. For example, moss plants only grow in very wet places. This is because mosses do not have roots to take water from the ground. Their leaves are also thin and lose water quickly. Plants that are adapted to drier environments have roots, a waxy waterproof **cuticle** on their leaves and **xylem vessels** (tubes that carry water).

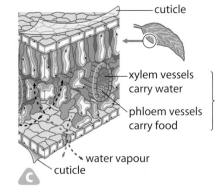

cuticle

xylem vessels carry water

phloem vessels carry food

vein

water vapour

cuticle

C

D Plants can be classified into four main groups.

Mosses:
• no roots
• no xylem
• small, flat, thin leaves
• no cuticle

Ferns:
• roots
• xylem
• many small leaves
• cuticle

plant kingdom

Conifers:
• roots
• xylem
• needle-shaped leaves
• thick cuticle

Flowering plants:
• roots
• xylem
• large, flat leaves
• cuticle

Scientists do not need to find whole fossil plants or even whole leaves to tell what plants were living in an area. Fossilised **seeds** and **spores** can be used instead. Conifers and flowering plants reproduce using seeds. Ferns and mosses reproduce using much smaller spores.

 E *Conifer seeds are found in* **cones**. *Flowering plant seeds are found in* **fruits**.

spores

spore containers

 F *Moss spore containers grow on stalks. Fern spore containers are under their leaves.*

Plants and extinction theories

If plants get too hot, they can lose too much water and die. If the Earth's atmosphere heated up too much this might explain why many plants became extinct.

All plants make their own food (glucose) using **photosynthesis**. Plants need water and carbon dioxide as raw materials and light energy to make photosynthesis happen. If the Earth's surface became very dark this would stop photosynthesis.

6 Look back at the two main theories about dinosaur extinction on pages 50–51. How can each theory explain why many plants became extinct? Ⓗ Ⓢ Ⓦ

7 A geologist finds moss spores in a rock layer. There are fossilised seeds in the layer above it. How did the environment change in this area? Ⓗ Ⓢ Ⓦ

3 a What do xylem vessels do?
 b Why don't moss leaves have veins in them?

4 How are conifers adapted to living in drier environments than mosses?

5 Look at photo A. What plant group is the leaf from? Ⓗ Ⓢ Ⓦ

Ⓗ Ⓢ Ⓦ
Classification is very important to scientists. Try to design a classification system to group plants that live in and around water (e.g. water lilies, pondweed, reeds).
○ How will you decide which plants to use?
○ How will you find information about the plants' features?

!
Trees can be conifers or flowering plants. The tallest flowering plants in the world are eucalyptus trees in Tasmania. They can grow up to 150 m tall.

I CAN...
○ recall the main features of the four different plant groups.
○ describe how plant fossils provide evidence for the extinction of plants and changes in environments. Ⓗ Ⓢ Ⓦ

8Db Detective work

How is evidence about populations and communities collected?

The animals and plants in a habitat are a **community**. The number of individuals of one species is its **population**.

Information about prehistoric communities and populations comes from fossils. For living organisms, **ecologists** use various ways to count plants and animals.

> **1 a** List the organisms in the community in photo A.
> **b** Which organisms had the largest population?
> **c** What is the evidence for your answer to part **b**?

Counting organisms is difficult if there are lots of them or they are hard to find. So, instead of counting all the organisms, scientists take **samples** (they look at what is in a small part of a habitat). The samples are used to **estimate** populations.

Many samples are taken because organisms are not spread evenly in a habitat. Different organisms prefer slightly different environments and so have an **uneven distribution**.

Different ways of sampling

A **quadrat** is a square used to take samples to count plants. It is thrown randomly about the habitat. Each time it lands, the plants inside it are counted.

Small animals from trees are collected using **tree beating**. A branch is shaken and the animals fall onto a sheet. The animals in tall grass can be collected with a **sweepnet**. Animals in leaves can be collected using a Tullgren funnel. A sample of leaves is put into the funnel. The small animals have a behaviour that makes them move away from heat and light. They fall into a beaker where they can be examined and counted.

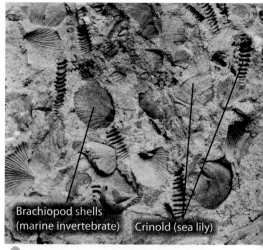

Brachiopod shells (marine invertebrate)   Crinold (sea lily)

A *Fossils from a river habitat about 500 million years ago.*

> **2** A 2 m² sample of lawn has 46 daisy plants. Estimate the number in 100 m².

How could you estimate how many steel tacks are buried in a tray of sand?
- How will you remove the tacks?
- How many samples will you take?

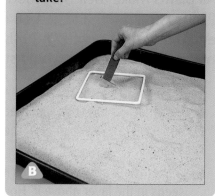

B

C *A Tullgren funnel.*

Photo D shows **pond dipping** – taking samples of water organisms by putting a net or jar into parts of a pond.

When fishing boats use nets, it is like pond dipping. Marjorie Courtenay-Latimer (1907–2004) worked for a museum in Cape Town, South Africa. She regularly inspected the fish that the boats caught. While doing this on 23rd December 1938, she found a coelacanth – a fish thought to have died out 80 million years ago!

Photo F shows a **pitfall trap**. This is a container buried in the ground. Animals fall into it. This is most often used for small animals.

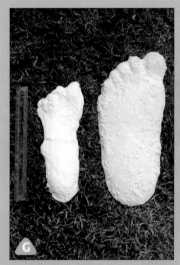

To study animal tracks and footprints scientists may make plaster casts of the prints. The casts in photo G are supposed to come from undiscovered giant apes living in America.

3 a How would you collect samples of animals living in trees?
  b How would you collect small animals that crawl along the ground?
4 How is fishing with nets like pond dipping?
5 What evidence do you think scientists had for thinking that coelacanths had become extinct?
6 The evidence for communities and populations collected using samples from existing habitats is much more reliable than evidence from fossils. Suggest reasons why.

I CAN...

o use different ways of collecting evidence for communities and populations.

How do we detect changes in environments?

HowScienceWorks

Changes in physical environmental factors can cause changes in communities, populations and distributions. Some of the equipment used to detect these changes can be connected to computers, which automatically record data and send it to a laboratory.

Ecologists find out how changes in environmental factors affect communities and populations. They also look for relationships between environmental factors. For example, fast-flowing water is normally colder than still water because the Sun does not get as much chance to warm it up.

When environments change organisms may no longer be able to survive in their habitats.

B *Corals are adapted to a certain water temperature. If the water gets too warm they turn white and die.*

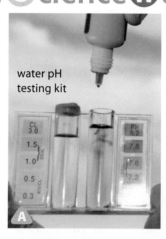

water pH testing kit

A

anemometer
to measure wind speed

How would you look for a relationship between the amount of light and the temperature in different environments?

1 List two physical environmental factors.

2 How do computers make collecting data easier?

When ecologists find out something interesting, they tell other ecologists. They may write a report called a paper, or go to a conference and display a poster or give a talk, or they may write a webpage.

a new classification of the flowering plants

C

3 Explain how global warming causes coral to die.

4 Some people over-water their cacti. Why do you think this is bad for these plants?

5 Why is it important that ecologists watch for changes in habitats?

The oceans contain 99% of the available space on Earth for organisms to live. Scientists have explored less than 10% of them.

I CAN...

o explain how changes in physical environmental factors are measured.

o describe some effects of changes in environmental factors on populations and communities.

How do we find out how environments change? HowScienceWorks

Scientists work out how environmental factors have changed over millions of years by looking at plant fossils. More evidence comes from rocks. For example, scientists test rocks from volcanoes to find their ages. The amount of these rocks of the same age shows how many volcanoes there were on Earth at a particular time. Computers then use this information to estimate how much carbon dioxide the volcanoes added to the air. This is known as **computer modelling**.

In some places ice has formed layers over thousands of years. Ice traps air as it forms and scientists investigate this air to work out what the atmosphere was like. This information provides more evidence that can be added to the computer model.

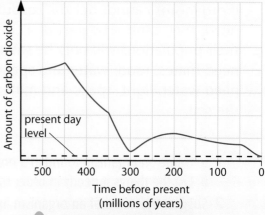

A *Computer model graph of carbon dioxide levels.*

Once scientists have evidence for how factors have changed in the past or in the present, they can also use computer models to make predictions.

B *These ice cores were drilled in Antarctica and contain ice up to 30 000 years old.*

C *This computer model allows scientists to predict the effect of global warming on sea levels.*

1 Suggest how a change in one physical environmental factor might have caused the extinction of the dinosaurs.

2 Fossilised cactus seeds have been found in Utah, USA which are 50 000 years old. What does this tell you about the environment of the area 50 000 years ago?

3 Fossils show that land plants spread across the Earth between 450 and 300 million years ago. Look at graph A. How does this computer model provide more evidence for this?

4 State two ways in which we can find out how much carbon dioxide was in the air 10 000 years ago.

5 Suggest a question that scientists might use the sea level computer model to answer as a prediction.

8Dd Living factors

How can living factors cause populations to change?

If organisms cannot get the **resources** they need, they cannot be part of a community, or their populations will only be small. Animals need mates, food, water and space. Plants need water, light, space and mineral salts from the soil.

> 1 a Name an organism found in a pond habitat.
>   b List the things it needs in order to survive.
> 2 Suggest the name of an organism in a woodland community that has:
>   a even distribution (found everywhere in the wood)
>   b uneven distribution.

A *Very few organisms can get the resources they need in this habitat. These ecologists need to bring resources with them.*

Physical environmental factors affect what organisms are in a community, the sizes of their populations and their distribution. For example, when it gets cold in winter, birds like swallows **migrate** and their population decreases. They find warmer areas where there is more food. Swallow migration is a behaviour that is partly automatic (**innate**) and partly **learned**. The stimulus for swallows to automatically start to migrate is the weather getting colder but they learn which way to go from other swallows.

Living factors are organisms that affect other organisms around them. Living factors can also change populations.

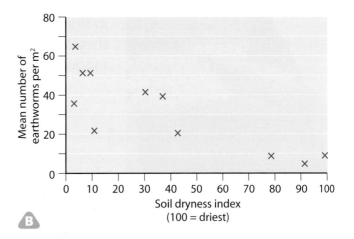

B

> 3 a Describe the trend in graph B. Ⓗ Ⓢ Ⓦ
>   b Use the graph to predict where the earthworm population would be larger – in wet woodland or dry woodland?
>   c Robins eat earthworms. How would the population of earthworms change if a lot of robins moved into a wood?

In Northern Canada lynxes eat snowshoe hares. When there are lots of hares, the lynxes have lots to eat. They reproduce successfully and their population goes up. When there are fewer hares, the lynx population decreases – some starve and others migrate.

4 Look at graph C.
  a Which animal is the **predator** and which is the **prey**?
  b Suggest how the change in a living factor might increase the hare population.
  c List three things that might decrease the lynx population.

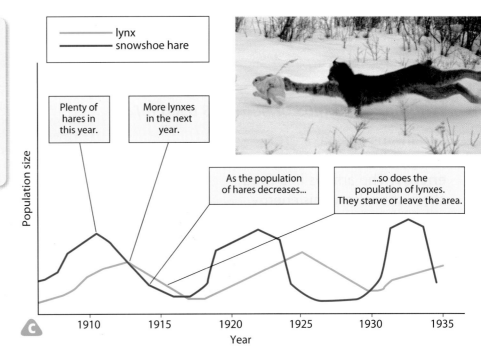

lynx
snowshoe hare

Population size

Plenty of hares in this year.

More lynxes in the next year.

As the population of hares decreases...

...so does the population of lynxes. They starve or leave the area.

1910   1915   1920   1925   1930   1935
Year

C

Organisms are in **competition** with one another for the resources they need. The organisms which are best adapted to get the resources are more likely to survive and reproduce. The others may migrate or die.

We can see how animals compete by looking at what eats what (the **feeding relationships**) in a **food web**. In food web D, grasshoppers and rabbits compete for grass. If the rabbits get a disease and die, there will be more grass. The population of the grasshoppers may then increase.

5 a What do foxes eat?   H S W
  b Write down the longest food chain in food web D.
  c Describe each organism in your food chain using these words:
    carnivore consumer herbivore omnivore producer top predator
  d Badgers eat insects and fruit. Which words in part **c** describe a badger?

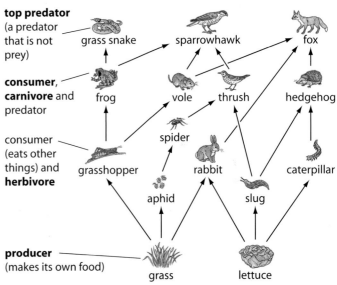

top predator (a predator that is not prey) — grass snake   sparrowhawk   fox

consumer, carnivore and predator — frog   vole   thrush   hedgehog

consumer (eats other things) and **herbivore** — grasshopper   spider   rabbit   caterpillar

aphid   slug

producer (makes its own food) — grass   lettuce

D A garden food web.

Organisms depend on each other for things besides food. For example, birds use trees for shelter and plants use animal waste to help them grow (it contains mineral salts).

6 Use food web D to predict what might happen to the slug population if: H S W
  a the caterpillars all die   b there is no rain for a long time
  c the spiders all die.

I CAN...
  o describe some effects of changes in living factors on populations and communities.
  o describe how organisms compete with one another.
  o use a food web to make predictions.   H S W

What are pyramids of numbers used for?

Organisms contain stored energy called **chemical energy**. The arrows in a food chain show how this energy passes from organism to organism. Normally there are fewer organisms as you go along a food chain because energy is lost at each stage.

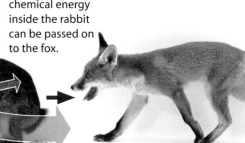

A lot of chemical energy in the food is released by respiration to let the rabbit move and keep warm.

Only some of the chemical energy is used for growth. Only the chemical energy inside the rabbit can be passed on to the fox.

A lot of the chemical energy is passed out in undigested food.

1 Why do animals respire?

A

Pyramids of numbers

Energy losses at each stage of the food chain mean that hundreds of lettuce plants only feed a much smaller number of rabbits. These rabbits feed an even smaller number of foxes. The numbers of different organisms at each stage of a food chain can be shown using a **pyramid of numbers**.

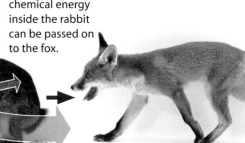

fox (secondary consumer)

rabbits (primary consumer)

lettuce plants (producer)

B A pyramid of numbers. Each level has a name (the **primary consumer** is the first animal that eats other organisms, the **secondary consumer** is the second one).

2 Think up another food chain and sketch a pyramid of numbers for it.

Pyramids of numbers do not look like pyramids if the organisms have very different sizes. For example, many aphids can feed on one rose bush.

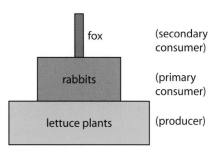

ladybirds

aphids

rose bush

C

3 Look at the food chain below.

grass → grasshopper → frog → grass snake
100 000   500   5   1

a Sketch a pyramid of numbers for the food chain. Ⓗ Ⓢ Ⓦ

b Draw a table to show the names of the top predator, the consumers, the producer, the primary consumer, the secondary consumer, the tertiary consumer, the herbivore, the carnivores.

4 Explain why diagram D is not shaped like a pyramid.

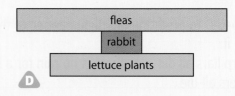

fleas

rabbit

lettuce plants

D

Damaging food webs

Macquarie Island, near Australia, is home to wandering albatrosses. The population of these birds was decreasing due to cats, rats and rabbits introduced by fishermen. The cats eat the young birds, the rats eat their eggs and the rabbits destroy nesting sites. In 2000, ecologists removed the last cat but this caused a large increase in the rats and rabbits. Ecologists are now planning to poison the rabbits and rats.

Using poisons can cause problems. Farmers use chemicals (**pesticides**) to kill organisms that eat or ruin their crops (**pests**). However, pesticides affect more animals than just the pests.

DDT is an insect pesticide (**insecticide**). It is not destroyed inside organisms and so passes along food chains. It caused the shells of top predator birds to be weak and break easily and was banned in 1984.

E *Wandering albatrosses are* **endangered***. They have the widest wingspan of any bird – up to 3.5 metres.*

Fields are sprayed with DDT to kill pests. It soaks into earthworms in the ground.

Blackbirds eat many earthworms so get a lot of DDT but not enough to cause much harm.

Peregrine falcons eat many blackbirds so get a very large dose of DDT. This causes their eggs to break.

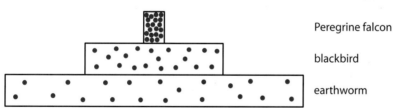

Peregrine falcon

blackbird

earthworm

F *Each dot represents a dose of DDT. The poison gets more concentrated further along the food chain.*

5 a Why are ecologists trying to remove rats and rabbits from Macquarie Island? Ⓗ Ⓢ Ⓦ
   b What effect did removing the cats have?
   c Why did it have this effect?

6 Look at food web D on page 59. A farmer uses a pesticide to kill the slugs. Explain how this will affect: Ⓗ Ⓢ Ⓦ
   a the hedgehog population
   b the spider population.

In 1962 Rachel Carson (1907–1964) warned people about the dangers of pesticides in a famous book called *Silent Spring*. Until that time, many people thought that pesticides were perfectly safe.

7 What do the following words mean? Give an example of each.
   a pest   b pesticide
8 Explain why the sparrowhawk population in the UK decreased in the 1970s.
9 Why do you think Rachel Carson's book was called *Silent Spring*?

I CAN...

o use pyramids of numbers to describe how energy is lost in a food chain.
o explain how humans can damage food chains.

How Science works

How can we stop organisms becoming endangered?

Many organisms have become extinct due to humans hunting, clearing habitats, introducing new species into habitats or using poisons. Dodos became extinct because they were hunted for food; their habitat was destroyed to plant crops; and the cats, pigs, goats and rats that sailors brought with them ate their eggs.

In the 1970s governments from 80 countries got together and made an agreement called CITES. This made it illegal to trade endangered organisms (or their parts) in those countries.

Individuals can also make decisions. Catching whole shoals of fish like tuna is **non-sustainable** since it kills the whole of the shoal (and other animals that get caught up in the net). So some people choose to buy 'rod-and-line caught' tuna, which is more expensive.

A In 1888, to protect farmers' sheep, hunters in Tasmania were rewarded for killing thylacine. The last one in the world died in a zoo in 1936.

B The trade of skins of endangered animals is illegal in Europe. This coat was confiscated by German customs officials.

C There are different species of tuna. Since the 1970s the bluefin tuna population has fallen by 70% due to **overfishing**.

HAVE YOUR SAY

Mink are farmed for their fur, which is used to make coats. They are not endangered. Mink farming was banned in the UK in 2003. Some people want to start mink farming again. What do you think of this idea?

D

1 a Animals can become extinct in many ways. List as many of these as you can.
 b Suggest some ways in which we can stop extinctions.

2 How is fishing for tuna with a rod and line **sustainable**?

3 a How does CITES help stop organisms from becoming extinct?
 b Find out what CITES stands for.

Using water

We all need water for drinking, cooking and washing ourselves and our clothes. Some people also water their gardens and wash their cars. On average, each person in the UK uses around 150 litres of water a day.

The water that people in developed countries use comes out of taps. The water is taken from lakes, rivers or wells. It is treated to make it clean and safe to use. When used water is let out of sinks or toilets are flushed, the water runs into a sewerage system, where it is treated again to make it safe.

A

B *Clean water coming out of a water treatment works.*

We cannot use water from the sea for drinking, because sea water has salt dissolved in it. The salty water would make us ill.

In some parts of the developing world, people have to get water from a well and carry it to their houses. In other places, people use water directly from rivers. Drinking water from rivers can spread diseases.

C

1 Write down five different things you use water for each day.
2 Draw a labelled diagram of the water cycle to explain how the water that comes from taps originally came from the sea.
3 Why can't we use sea water for drinking?
4 Water from rivers or lakes may have mud or leaves and sticks in it. Explain how filters and sieves can remove these things from the water.

8Ea The solution is clear

What happens when things are mixed together?

If lots of different things are jumbled up together, we have a **mixture**.

Sea water is a mixture. It is mostly water, but it has many different chemicals in it, including salt. It also has rubbish, seaweed and sand in it.

A

> 1 What is a mixture?
> 2 Make a list of the different things in the mixture in photo A.

Seaweed and sand can be separated from sea water by **filtering**. The seaweed and sand are trapped in the filter paper, but the water runs through it.

> 3 How does a filter work?

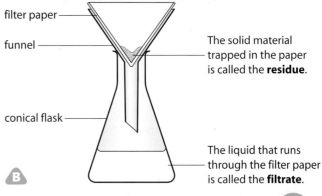

filter paper

funnel

The solid material trapped in the paper is called the **residue**.

conical flask

The liquid that runs through the filter paper is called the **filtrate**.

B

Filtering will not separate the salt from the sea water, because the salt has **dissolved** in the water. When salt is stirred into water the salt grains seem to disappear. They break into very tiny pieces and mix with the water. A substance that dissolves is said to be **soluble**. Something that will not dissolve is said to be **insoluble**.

A solid dissolved in a liquid makes a **solution**. In a solution the liquid is called the **solvent**, and the solid is called the **solute**.

H S W

You can only taste substances that dissolve in the moisture on your tongue. You cannot taste insoluble substances.

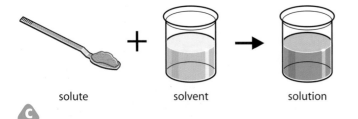

solute   solvent   solution

C

> 4 Write down the name of:
>   a two solids that dissolve in water
>   b a solid that does not dissolve in water.
> 5 In a cup of instant coffee:
>   a what is the solvent
>   b what is the solute?

You can't always get clean water from a tap. Survival experts have to make their own clean water.

○ Design a piece of equipment that you could use to make clean (**colourless**) water in the countryside.

D

A solution is always **transparent** (see-through). If a liquid is cloudy or **opaque**, then it is not a solution.

beaker 1   beaker 2   beaker 3

E

Water is not the only solvent. Nail varnish does not dissolve in water, but it does dissolve in a liquid called propanone, which is in nail varnish remover. Some paints can be washed off with water, but gloss paint cannot. A solvent called white spirit is used to remove gloss paint. Gloss paint is soluble in white spirit but not in water.

F   These sand filters are used to clean water before it is recycled back to the environment.

6 How can you tell if:
   a a solid has dissolved
   b a solid has not dissolved?

7 a Describe the three liquids in photo E. Include the words transparent and opaque in your descriptions. H S W
   b Which beaker(s) contain a solution?
   c Explain your answer to part **b**.

I CAN...

○ recall the words used to describe mixtures and solutions.
○ describe how filtering works.
○ explain why filtering will not separate a solute from a solution.

What happens when something dissolves?

When you make a solution, the solute does not go away. All the solute you use stays in the solution. The total mass of a solution is always equal to the mass of solvent added to the mass of solute.

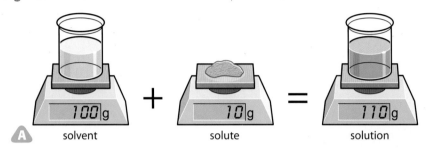

A   solvent   +   solute   =   solution

We can explain what happens using ideas about particles.

> 1 You add 2 g of salt to 20 g of water. What will the mass of the solution be?

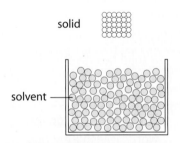

solid

solvent

B The particles in a solid are all held together in a fixed arrangement.

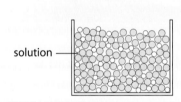

solution

C When the solid dissolves, the particles come away from each other. They mix with the particles in the solvent.

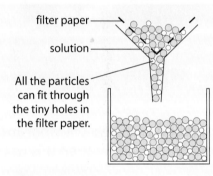

filter paper

solution

All the particles can fit through the tiny holes in the filter paper.

D The particles of the solid are too small to be trapped by the filter paper. This is why filtering cannot separate a dissolved solid from a liquid.

2 a How are particles held together in a solid?
  b What happens to the particles when the solid dissolves?
3 Why can't you use a filter to separate salt from water?   H S W
4 Draw a particle diagram to show what happens when you filter salty water that has sand in it.   H S W

There are very few things that are totally insoluble, although the amount that dissolves might be very small. Even sand dissolves! Sand is made of a chemical called silica. 0.1 g of silica will dissolve in a litre of water. Sponges can extract the silica from sea water and use it to help build their bodies.

Sea water contains about 35 g of dissolved salt for every 100 g of water. Drinking water contains less than 1 g of dissolved salt for every 100 g water.

Even soluble solids like sugar cannot keep on dissolving forever. For example, you wouldn't expect a whole bag of sugar to dissolve in a glass of water. You could find out how much sugar will dissolve in a glass of water by adding it a little at a time. Eventually you would find that no more sugar will dissolve.

When no more sugar will dissolve, there will be some crystals left at the bottom of the glass. The solution is now **saturated**. It contains as much dissolved solid as it possibly can. If you add more sugar, it will sink to the bottom and stay undissolved.

In the first beaker in photo F, 34 g of solid have dissolved in 100 cm³ of water to make a saturated solution. The **solubility** of this solid is 34 g per 100 cm³ of water. The second beaker has twice as much water, so twice the mass of solid will dissolve (68 g).

The temperature also affects the amount of a solid that dissolves. For most solids, more solid dissolves when the water is hotter.

How could you find out if more salt or more sugar dissolves in water?
- What would you measure?
- How would you make it a fair test?

How could you show that the solubility of salt or sugar changes with temperature?
- How would you measure the solubility at different temperatures?

5 Write down two variables that affect the amount of solid needed to make a saturated solution.

6 Milk of Magnesia® is an indigestion remedy that contains magnesium oxide. How can you tell from the picture that not all of the magnesium oxide has dissolved? H S W

I CAN...

- explain what happens to particles when a solid dissolves. H S W
- use ideas about particles to explain why filtering cannot be used to separate a solvent and a solute. H S W
- explain what a saturated solution is.
- describe some variables that affect the amount of solute that dissolves.

How can we find out what is dissolved in water?

Most water isn't just water. Water dissolves chemicals from rocks as it flows over them and these dissolved chemicals give the water its taste. Different rocks contain different chemicals and so the taste of the water depends on where it comes from.

We can show that the water contains these chemicals by heating it. The water will **evaporate** and leave behind the chemicals that were dissolved in it. If we evaporate different water samples, we will get different amounts of these chemicals.

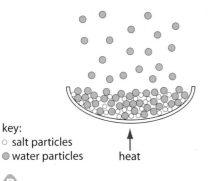

key:
○ salt particles
● water particles   ↑ heat

B

The chemicals that are left behind are called **salts**. Our bodies need salts to stay healthy.

A *These whiskys all taste different because they are made with water from different places.*

1 Why do different samples of water have different tastes?

2 How can you get salt from salty water? H S W

H S W

How could you test different samples of water to find out which ones contained the most salt?

o How would you make your test fair?

 !

H S W

Salts are important for a healthy diet and for preserving food. Roman soldiers used to receive common salt as part of their pay. Our word 'salary' comes from 'sal' – the Latin word for salt.

*The companies who supply our water take samples regularly. The samples are tested in a laboratory to make sure they meet **quality standards**. The standards are set by the government to make sure our drinking water is safe.*

C

In some parts of the country the water contains certain chemicals that stop soap making a lather. This water is described as **hard water**. Water that does not contain these chemicals is called **soft water**.

> 3 a What causes hard water?
>   b Some people use 'water softeners' to remove the chemicals that cause hard water. Suggest why they do this.

Producing salt

We can get lots of salt from sea water if we let the heat of the Sun evaporate the water for us. The main salt in sea water is a chemical called sodium chloride, often called **common salt**, or just 'salt'.

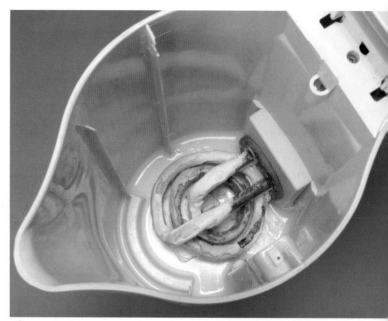

D Hard water forms scum on boiled water, and 'furs up' kettles and central heating pipes.

E Collecting salt made from the evaporation of sea water in France. This is called the salt-bed method.

In Cheshire, England, salt is found in thick layers underground. This **rock salt** can be mined leaving large caverns. The salt can also be removed by pumping water into the ground. This water dissolves the salt, making salt solution or **brine**. The brine is then pumped back to the surface and heated to evaporate the water.

> H S W
>
> How could you get the salt from a mixture of rock and salt, using the apparatus in your laboratory?

> 4 How does the Sun help us to get salt?
> 5 The sea has salt dissolved in it.   H S W
>   a Where has this salt come from?
>   b How did it get into the sea?
> 6 Imagine that you work for a company which makes salt by evaporating sea water using the salt-bed method. Describe your job and give details of the difficulties of getting salt in this way.   H S W

I CAN...

o explain how to find out how much salt is in water.   H S W

o describe how salt can be obtained from sea water or from mines.   H S W

8Ed What's in a solution?

How can mixtures of dissolved solids be separated?

If you evaporate a liquid, any solutes that were dissolved in the liquid will be left behind. The solutes will be mixed up. **Chromatography** is a way of separating different substances that are dissolved in a solution.

Chromatography can be used to find out what colours are mixed together in different paints, dyes and inks. Each paint or ink mixture will make a different pattern.

> 1 Why can't you just evaporate a liquid to find out which substances were dissolved in it?

A

The liquids to be tested are dropped onto special paper. The bottom of the paper is dipped in water. Diagram B shows five different dyes being tested.

Different chemicals are made of particles of different sizes. When they are dissolved in a liquid, the different-sized particles travel through special paper at different speeds and so they separate out at different distances. If a dye does not dissolve in water, a different solvent can be used.

- rod holding paper
- chromatography paper
- beaker
- pencil line
    X Y A B C
- water

B At the start…

    X Y A B C

C …and after the solvent has soaked up the paper.

The **chromatogram** in diagram C shows that liquid X contained two dyes. It is a mixture of dyes B and C.

> 2 Why do different substances travel different distances in chromatography? Ⓗ Ⓢ Ⓦ
> 3 a How many different dyes were in liquid Y? Ⓗ Ⓢ Ⓦ
>   b Which dye(s) were they?   c Explain your answers.
> 4 The ink shown in photo D is a mixture of different colours. Ⓗ Ⓢ Ⓦ
>   a How many different colours are mixed together in the ink?
>   b Name these colours.

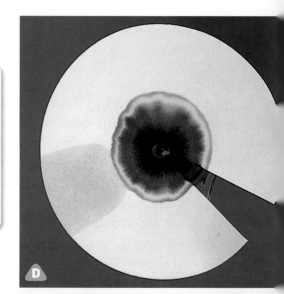

D

Police have found a letter written in coloured felt-tipped pen at the scene of a crime. Five people are suspects because they have the same coloured pen. How could you find out which felt-tipped pen was used to write the letter?

o How will you get the ink off the original paper?

o How will you compare it with inks from the other five pens?

o How will you make it a fair test?

Chromatography is often used by the police in their investigations. For example, samples of blood or skin are collected from the scene of a crime. Certain chemicals in these samples are compared with those from a suspect, using chromatography. If the samples match, it proves that the suspect was at the scene of the crime.

E *A scientist comparing 'DNA fingerprints'.*

The use of chromatography to identify criminals is called 'DNA fingerprinting'. It was invented in 1984 by Alec Jeffreys (1950–) who is Professor of Genetics at the University of Leicester, England. Today, most chromatography is done by machines and the results are shown on a computer screen. Machines can even carry out chromatography on chemicals that are not coloured.

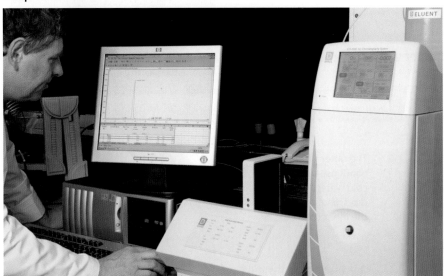

F *Chromatography can be used to analyse samples of water to find out how much of certain chemicals are in the water.*

5 Picture G shows what happened when different orange squashes and food colourings were tested using chromatography.

G

a Which food colourings are found in the three kinds of orange squash?

b Tartrazine is thought to make some people over-active. Which orange squash would be safe to give to an over-active person? Explain your answer.

c Why do you think Tartrazine is added to some orange squashes?

I CAN...

o describe what chromatography is and what it is used for.

o use ideas about particles to explain how chromatography works.

How can we make pure water?

Pure water contains nothing but water. To get pure water, we must take the water out of the solution, leaving everything else behind. The first step in doing this is to heat the solution.

When salty water is heated, the liquid turns into a gas called **steam** or **water vapour**. This process is called evaporation. The salt particles do not evaporate and are left behind. If the steam is collected and cooled, it turns back into a liquid. This is called **condensing**. The condensed water will be pure because the salt particles are no longer mixed with it.

> 1 What is pure water?

A Steam irons often need to be filled with pure water and not tap water. This is because the salts in tap water get left behind when the water evaporates and clog up the iron.

> 2 a What happens to the particles in water when they evaporate?
> b What is condensing? Ⓗ Ⓢ Ⓦ
> 3 What is another name for water vapour?

The water vapour rises and then goes down the inner tube of the Liebig condenser.

thermometer

cold water out

The outer tube of the condenser is filled with cold water flowing from a tap. The outer tube keeps the inner tube cold.

In the condenser the water vapour is cooled and condenses into a liquid.

The flask contains inky water. When the flask is heated the water turns into water vapour, leaving the dissolved ink particles behind.

cold water in

Pure (distilled) water runs into the beaker.

heat

B

This process of separating a solvent from solutes by evaporating the solvent and then condensing it is called **distillation**. The whole set of apparatus used is called a **still**.

Ⓗ Ⓢ Ⓦ

C This version of a still is called an alembic. It was invented in about 800 CE by the Arab chemist Jabir ibn Hayyan (c.721–c.815). Alembics made from copper are still in use today.

> 4 Suggest why a Liebig condenser might work better than an alembic. Ⓗ Ⓢ Ⓦ

Stills can also use energy from the Sun. In 1872, Charles Wilson invented a solar-powered water still. It was a cheap way of providing clean water in poor areas of the world. Diagram D shows how it works.

Today solar-powered stills can be important for providing emergency clean water supplies in remote places and at sea. The still in photo E can be floated on the sea.

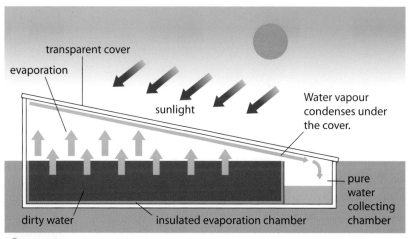

D A basin solar still.

5 Explain why a solar-powered water still might be useful: Ⓗ Ⓢ Ⓦ
  a on a boat that has broken down at sea
  b in a country where the drinking water contains bacteria which cause diseases.
6 Explain how a solar-powered water still works. Ⓗ Ⓢ Ⓦ

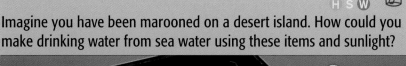

Ⓗ Ⓢ Ⓦ

Imagine you have been marooned on a desert island. How could you make drinking water from sea water using these items and sunlight?

I CAN...

o explain what pure water is.
o describe how to distil water. Ⓗ Ⓢ Ⓦ
o explain why distillation produces pure water. Ⓗ Ⓢ Ⓦ

How can water companies supply enough drinking water?

How Science Works

Water for many places in the UK comes from a nearby river or a local lake or reservoir. The water is treated before it is supplied to consumers. However, local rivers cannot always supply enough water for big cities.

In the 1830s Manchester was a growing industrial town. There was not enough water for the people to drink and to use in the factories. Manchester Corporation built a set of reservoirs in the nearby Pennine hills, which were completed in 1851. However, this was not enough and in 1894 a new dam across Thirlmere, in the Lake District, was completed. Water from the Thirlmere reservoir was carried in underground pipes nearly 100 miles south to Manchester. Manchester continued to grow, and between 1919 and 1935 another dam was built to create Haweswater. Two villages were demolished so that the valley could be flooded.

A *Thirlmere.*

B *You can sometimes see the remains of the village of Mardale Green when the water level in the Haweswater reservoir is very low.*

Some countries do not get enough water from rainfall. If the country is near the sea, drinking water can be made from sea water. To do this, they must remove the salt from the water. This is known as **desalination**.

One way of desalinating water is by distillation. The water is filtered to remove any insoluble particles and then boiled in a large tank. The steam rises, leaving the salt behind, and goes through a pipe into a heat exchanger. The heat exchanger takes heat away from the steam and the steam condenses into pure water. The water can be bottled or piped to towns and cities.

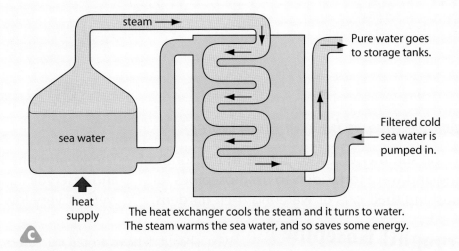

The heat exchanger cools the steam and it turns to water. The steam warms the sea water, and so saves some energy.

A desalination plant needs a lot of energy to boil large volumes of sea water. In some countries the Sun's energy (solar power) is used to make the water boil. In other areas oil or gas is burned to provide the heat, but this makes the water much more expensive to produce. A more modern method, called 'reverse osmosis', does not need quite as much energy.

Cruise ships and submarines also use desalination plants. The Queen Mary 2 can produce nearly 1900 tons of water each day from sea water.

1 Suggest some advantages and disadvantages of creating a reservoir for:
   a wildlife
   b people living in the valley that the reservoir will fill
   c people living in the area near the reservoir
   d people living in cities.

2 Rather than build huge reservoirs to allow cities to grow bigger, people could live in smaller towns with their own local water supplies.
   a Suggest some advantages and disadvantages of this situation.
   b What would some of the difficulties be in making this happen?

3 Suggest reasons for the following statements. You may need to look up some information to help you.
   a A cruise ship is more likely to have a desalination plant than a cargo ship.
   b The only desalination plants in the UK at the moment are in Jersey and the Scilly Isles. (You may need to look up these places on a map.)
   c Water supply companies in the south-east of England are trying out small desalination plants. (Find out how many people live in the south-east compared to other parts of the UK.)

Will we always have enough water?

In the summer of 2006, people in the south of England were forbidden to use hosepipes for washing their cars or watering their gardens.

The weather had been very dry for a while, and reservoirs and rivers that supplied the area were at very low levels.

'Drought! Hosepipe bans in south-east!'

Why should I have to let my plants die, when the people at the golf course still water their grass?

We don't need drinking-quality water to flush the loo or water the garden. If people saved the water from their bath or shower, or collected rainwater, we wouldn't need to use as much treated water.

Lots of treated water leaks out of underground pipes. The water companies should fix their pipes before they start asking us to go without!

It takes thousands of litres of water to make one car. Maybe the people in industry should use less!

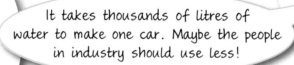

HAVE YOUR SAY

How should the government make sure that the UK has enough water?
- Should people use less?
- Should the government build more reservoirs and pipelines?

1 a What could be in water from a lake?
  b How could this water be treated to remove solid material from it?
  c Why won't this method remove substances dissolved in the water?
  d Describe how you could remove dissolved substances from the water.

2 How could the government:
  a try to persuade people to use less water
  b make people use less water
  c get the water companies to waste less water?

How**S**cience**w**orks

Every year, we are using up more of the planet's resources. We have to be more efficient in the way that we use materials now and in the future to avoid running out. Most councils have a **recycling** collection scheme which covers paper and card, metals, glass and plastics.

> 1 Name four materials that can be recycled.

A *Materials for recycling need to be sorted in a recycling centre.*

In science, we **classify** materials in a number of different ways according to their properties, for example as solids, liquids and gases. At a recycling facility, the mixture of materials that is collected has to be sorted before being sent off for reprocessing so that items can be used again. Firstly, the different materials have to be separated. Then, the different types of each material may also need to be separated, for example newspaper from cardboard, and PET plastic from polythene plastic.

2 At a recycling centre, what categories would they use to sort different types of:
 a glass b metal?

3 a Describe the recycling scheme that operates in your area.
 b How do you think this would compare to other parts of the UK, and to other countries across the world?
 c How would you rate your school for recycling?
 d Suggest some practical ideas that could improve the recycling rate either at school or at home.

4 Think of a plus, a minus and an interesting point about this statement: all glass should be recycled.

How were the different elements discovered?

Thousands of years ago people only knew about a few metals like gold and silver. These metals occur naturally and can be found as tiny pieces in streams. The metals were very valuable because they were rare and so they were **recycled** by melting them down and making them into new objects.

Later it was discovered that heating certain types of rocks in a charcoal fire formed copper, which became widely available. The rocks are called copper **ores**. Some ores contain other metals such as tin. Bronze (a mixture of copper and tin) was probably discovered by accident. It is stronger and easier to melt than pure copper. Bronze was discovered about 5000 years ago in Egypt and was the most important metal for around 2000 years.

> **1** Name three metals that were used 3000 years ago.

A *This 'Rhodanian' dagger is over 3000 years old and is made from bronze. The period when bronze was the most important metal is called the Bronze Age.*

H S W **!**

The Romans melted down the bronze statues that they found in areas that they invaded. They recycled the metal to make weapons or statues of Roman gods or emperors.

People found that using hotter fires could produce other materials. The first glass was made during the Bronze Age by heating sand. Bellows were invented in about 1500 BCE and were used to blow air into a flame to make it hotter. This allowed iron to be extracted from certain rocks and led to the Iron Age.

H S W **!**

Recycling has always been part of the history of paper. The first paper was made in China about 2000 years ago from old rags. In Japan, 1000 years ago, recycled paper (made from wastepaper) was highly prized. The first use of toilet paper is recorded in China in the year 589.

> **2** Glass and iron were often recycled in the Iron Age. Suggest why.
> **3** In which country were these first manufactured:
> a bronze b paper

A thousand years ago, Arabic **alchemists** (people interested in a connection between religion and science) started to experiment to make new chemicals, including acids. By the eighteenth century, chemists in Europe discovered that some substances, like gold and copper, could not be split into simpler substances by mixing them or heating them. These simple substances were called **elements**.

In 1789 the French chemist Antoine Lavoisier (1743–1794) published the first ever table of the elements, with 33 substances in it. Shortly after this, in 1799, the electric battery was invented. This gave scientists a new way to split up chemicals. Lime was split up using electricity in 1808. As a result, a metal called calcium was discovered. Until this time it had been thought that lime was an element.

Nicholas Flamel (c. 1332–1415) was an alchemist who lived in Paris. He claimed to have made the Philosopher's Stone, which allowed him to turn metals like lead into gold.

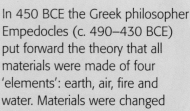

Noms nouveaux.	Noms anciens correspondans.
Lumière.........	Lumière.
Calorique........	Chaleur. Principe de la chaleur. Fluide igné. Feu. Matière du feu & de la chaleur.
Oxygène........	Air déphlogistiqué. Air empiréal. Air vital. Base de l'air vital.
Azote...........	Gaz phlogistiqué. Mofete. Base de la mofete.
Hydrogène.....	Gaz inflammable. Base du gaz inflammable.
Soufre..........	Soufre.
Phosphore........	Phosphore.
Carbone.........	Charbon pur.
Radical muriatique.	Inconnu.
Radical fluorique .	Inconnu.
Radical boracique,.	Inconnu.
Antimoine.......	Antimoine.
Argent..........	Argent.
Arsenic.........	Arsenic.
Bismuth.........	Bismuth.
Cobolt..........	Cobolt.
Cuivre..........	Cuivre.
Etain...........	Etain.
Fer.............	Fer.
Manganèse......	Manganèse.
Mercure........	Mercure.
Molybdène......	Molybdène.
Nickel..........	Nickel.
Or.............	Or.
Platine.........	Platine.
Plomb..........	Plomb.
Tungstène......	Tungstene.
Zinc...........	Zinc.
Chaux.........	Terre calcaire, chaux.
Magnésie........	Magnésie, base du sel d'Epsom.
Baryte.........	Barote, terre pesante.
Alumine........	Argile, terre de l'alun, base de l'alun.
Silice..........	Terre siliceuse, terre vitrifiable.

 Lavoisier's table of elements.

4 What is an element?

5 Which three of these substances are elements?
copper   glass   lime   calcium   bronze   sand   gold   paper

6 a Why did scientists think that lime was an element?
  b What evidence changed this view?

Today we know of 117 elements. About 90 of these make all the materials in the Universe. Chemists are constantly inventing new materials. If we can recycle more, we may be able to satisfy our demand for new materials without damaging the environment.

7 a In what order were calcium, gold and iron discovered? H S W
  b Explain why they were discovered in this order.

In 450 BCE the Greek philosopher Empedocles (c. 490–430 BCE) put forward the theory that all materials were made of four 'elements': earth, air, fire and water. Materials were changed when the elements joined in different ways under the influence of the forces of 'love' and 'hate'.

I CAN...

o describe what an element is.
o describe the contribution of different scientists and cultures to the discovery of useful materials. H S W

How do we represent different elements?

The word 'elementary' means simple. Elements are simple substances. You cannot split an element up into anything simpler using a chemical reaction. We can join the 26 letters of our alphabet together to make millions of different words. In a similar way, all the materials in the natural world can be made from about 90 of the elements. It is the way the elements are joined together that makes each material different. The particles that make up an element are called **atoms**. An atom is the smallest particle of an element that you can get.

H S W

Leucippus and Democritus, two Greek scientists living 2500 years ago, first had the idea that an atom was the smallest possible particle that couldn't be split up. The Greek word *atomos* means indivisible.

1 What is:
  a an element
  b an atom?

2 The **periodic table** is a list of all the elements we know about. Use the periodic table on page 182 of the book to help you find out which five of the substances in this list are elements:
gold   salt   air   mercury
iron   water   oxygen
aluminium   glass
polystyrene

scale: ×20 000 000

A *The aluminium in this can is made up of atoms. As aluminium is an element, all the atoms in the can are the same.*

scale: ×20 000 000

The steel in this can is made of two elements. Most of the can is made of iron, but there is a small amount of carbon as well. There are two different types of atom in steel. Steel is a **mixture***.*

3 How many different kinds of atom are there in: **a** aluminium **b** steel?
4 Brass is another metal that can be recycled. Brass is a mixture of about two-thirds copper and one-third zinc. Draw a particle diagram to show the arrangement of atoms in brass.

There are a number of different types of plastics. Each one has a recycling code on it to help us identify which type is which. Each different type of plastic has a code number and initials, so that you can identify the plastic even if you don't know the name. This code is used across Europe and America to identify plastics.

There is also a code for the chemical elements – each one has a **symbol**. The chemical symbols are an international code, used all over the world. Sometimes the symbol is the first letter of the name. The symbol for carbon is C and the one for oxygen is O. There are 117 elements and only 26 letters of the alphabet, so most elements have a two-letter code. For example, aluminium is Al and helium is He. Sometimes the letters do not match the name in English, but will match the names in other languages. Often, the symbols are taken from the original Latin, for example 'ferrum' for iron.

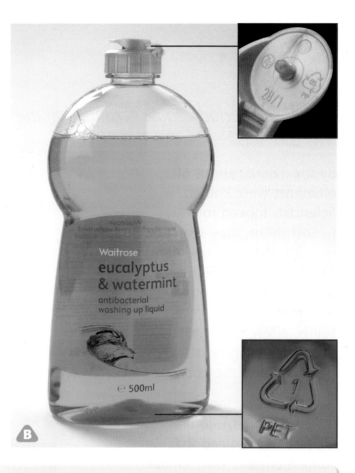

B

5 Look at the pictures below that show the names of five elements in different European languages. Use the symbols and the periodic table to look up the English names. ⒽⓈⓌ

a French = cuivre, symbol = Cu

b German = wolfram, symbol = W

c Spanish = estano, symbol = Sn

d Italian = ferro, symbol = Fe

e Greek = natrion, symbol = Na

C

6 Scrap metals are often separated into 'ferrous' and 'non-ferrous' metals.
   a Which element has the symbol Fe?
   b Why does it have this symbol?
   c Which of these metals is 'ferrous'? Choose from: aluminium, brass, bronze, steel.
   d Explain why this is a ferrous metal and why the others are non-ferrous.

7 Some elements are named after famous scientists. Find out: ⒽⓈⓌ
   a the names of the scientists who have had these elements named after them and
   b why the scientist is famous.
      i No   ii Es   iii Cm   iv Fm   v Md

I CAN...

o explain what atoms are.
o use a particle diagram to identify elements and mixtures. ⒽⓈⓌ
o use the periodic table to identify the chemical symbols for some elements. ⒽⓈⓌ
o explain that chemical symbols are an international code. ⒽⓈⓌ

Why is the periodic table arranged in the way that it is?

HowScienceWorks

By the 1860s, about 60 elements were known. Scientists looked for ways to sort them; they searched for patterns in the elements' properties. Most elements were metals, but some were non-metals. Most were solids, a few were gases, and there were only two liquids (bromine and mercury).

A number of scientists tried to find a pattern. Johann Döbereiner noticed that some elements with similar properties could be grouped in threes (triads). John Newlands put elements into groups of seven.

However, all the known elements didn't fit fully into either pattern and whenever anyone discovered a new element, it threw the whole system out. When he presented his 'Law of Octaves' at the Chemical Society in March 1866, very few scientists took Newlands seriously – one professor suggested that arranging elements in alphabetical order would give some 'patterns' by coincidence.

A Johann Döbereiner (1780–1849).

B John Newlands (1837–1898).

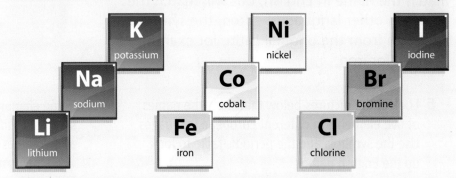

C Some of Döbereiner's triads: (1) the alkali metals (2) magnetic metals (3) the halogens – three dangerous non-metals.

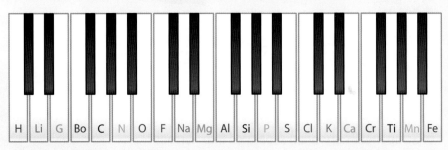

D John Newlands thought he had found groups of seven elements, which he called his octaves, like the notes of a musical scale.

1 a How many elements were in Lavoisier's original table of elements?
  b How many more elements were known by the 1860s?
2 Which scientist tried to group the elements into **a** triads? **b** octaves?

Dimitri Mendeleev was a Russian chemist who enjoyed playing cards. He made a pack of cards using the elements, which he numbered from the lightest mass to the heaviest mass. On 17 February 1869 he sat down to play a game of patience, dealing out the cards to try to get a pattern so that similar elements came together in columns. The result of his card game was basically the table that we use today, which is called the periodic table. He did three important things:

- He didn't try to make a totally regular grid – some rows were longer than others.
- If the elements didn't fit his table, he swapped the cards round and told the experimenters that they must have got the masses of the elements wrong!
- He left gaps for elements that he said had not been discovered yet – and predicted what they would be like!

Although not all of his ideas were correct, most of Mendeleev's predictions did come true, and his table of the elements was accepted as the best way of organising the elements. A modern version is shown on page 182.

E Dimitri Mendeleev (1834–1907).

F Mendeleev's original periodic table, which stands in the Russian city of St Petersburg as a monument to his work.

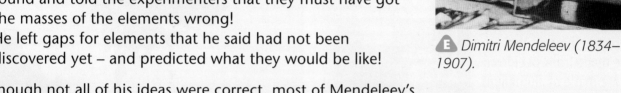

3 Compare Newlands' octaves with the modern periodic table. Which five elements have been discovered between hydrogen and iron since Newlands' time?

4 Explain how Mendeleev's table was able to cope with new discoveries more easily than Newlands' or Döbereiner's systems.

5 How could Mendeleev's table be used to predict the properties of elements that had not been discovered?

6 Explain why scientists find Mendeleev's table a more useful arrangement than a simple rectangular grid.

7 Do you think it was fair that John Newlands' ideas were not taken seriously at the time? Explain your answer by referring to the evidence.

8Fc Metal detecting

How can we tell if an element is a metal?

Scrap metals are big business. At a recycling centre, the different metals have to be separated from one another. **Metals** are separated using their different **properties**. For example, iron is **magnetic**. Most metals are not.

H S W

Design a can sorter to separate the cans that are made from steel from those made of aluminium.
o What variables might affect your design?

A can sorter. **B**

A

There are other ways we can tell if something is a metal. Metals are usually:

- **shiny**
- flexible
- good **heat conductors**
- solids at room temperature
- good **electrical conductors**.

C *Recycled fridges contain metals and non-metals.*

1 Write down three properties that most metals have.
2 Mercury is a metal that becomes a liquid at −39 °C. Why is this an unusual metal?
3 Look at the periodic table on page 182. Where are the metals and where are the non-metals?
4 a The three magnetic elements are iron, cobalt and nickel. What do you notice about the position of these three elements in the periodic table?
   b Copper, silver and gold are metals that are used for jewellery. Where do these metals come in the periodic table?

A fridge will contain plastics as well as metals. You will not find any plastics in the periodic table because all plastics are made from at least two elements. The elements that plastics are made from are not metals – they are **non-metals**. Non-metals have different properties to metals. Non-metals are often:

- gases or solids that melt very easily
- good heat and electrical **insulators**.

D *Sulphur is a non-metal. These sulphur crystals melt easily at just over 100 °C.*

Sulphur is a non-metal. These sulphur crystals melt easily at just over 100 °C. If you drop a lump of sulphur, it will break. Substances like sulphur and glass which shatter in this way are brittle.

Some non-metals are used in recycling. Oxygen and chlorine can both be used to bleach recycled paper. Chlorine is used less often because it is poisonous and is more harmful to the environment. We also use chlorine in swimming pools. The level of chlorine in the water needs to be just enough to kill harmful bacteria, but not so high that it makes your eyes sting.

5 a Look at photo E. What is the state of iodine at room temperature?
  b Photo F shows what happens when iodine is heated. What state is the iodine?
  c Why is this change unusual?
  d Is iodine a metal or a non-metal? Explain your reasoning.

6 What is the state of chlorine at room temperature?

7 Does chlorine dissolve in water easily? How can you tell?

8 What would be the problem in a swimming pool if the amount of chlorine added to the water was:
  a not enough
  b too much?

9 Describe which parts of the plug in photo H are made of metal and which parts are plastic. Explain why these materials have been chosen by referring to their properties.

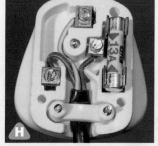

In the First World War, chlorine was used as a poison gas. It was denser than air and filled up the trenches, killing many soldiers.

 H S W

What tests could you carry out to decide if an element was a metal or a non-metal?
  o How many tests would you need to do?
  o Which results would be the most important?

I CAN...

o carry out tests to decide whether a substance is a metal or non-metal.
o describe the properties of metals and non-metals.
o explain why materials are used for particular jobs based on their properties. **H S W**

8Fd Compound interest

What happens when elements combine?

All fridges contain a liquid that circulates in the pipes. Before 1994, this liquid was usually Freon-12, a type of CFC (chlorofluorocarbon). When fridges were dumped, the CFC escaped into the air. Evidence started to build up that CFCs were damaging the atmosphere and helping to cause global warming. Now, all CFCs have to be recycled.

CFCs are made from non-metal elements. Diagram A shows a model of Freon-12. The three elements have joined together to form a **compound**. The smallest particle of Freon-12 contains two atoms of chlorine, two atoms of fluorine and one atom of carbon. This is called a **molecule**. We can show the number of atoms in a molecule by using the **chemical formula**. The chemical formula of this CFC is CF_2Cl_2.

A

1 Are each of the following elements or compounds?
  a carbon b fluorine c Freon-12
2 Another type of CFC, Freon-13, has the formula $CClF_3$.
  a How many different *elements* are there in Freon-13?
  b How many *atoms* are there in a molecule of Freon-13?
  c Draw a diagram of a molecule of Freon-13.

Most plastics are compounds made of carbon and hydrogen atoms joined together. This diagram shows polythene.

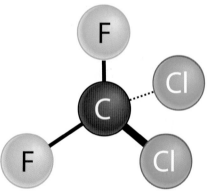

B A molecule of Freon-12.

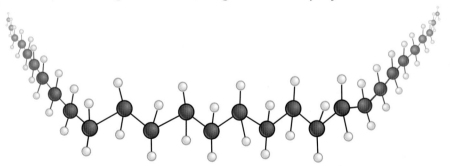

C A molecule of polythene.

It has too many atoms to count. If a compound does not exist as a small molecule its chemical formula shows the ratio of the elements in it. In polythene, there are two hydrogen atoms for each carbon atom and so the formula is CH_2.

3 PVC plastics have the formula C_2H_3Cl.
  a How many different elements are there in PVC?
  b Draw a section of a chain, similar to diagram C, showing how the atoms are arranged in PVC.

What's in a name?

Glass is another compound that does not exist as small molecules. So its formula is also a ratio – SiO_2. Its name is silicon dioxide. The 'ide' ending tells us that the compound contains two elements. The 'silicon' and the 'ox' tell us what those elements are. The 'di' means two.

Other **oxides** in a recycling plant include carbon dioxide (found in some gas cylinders) and iron oxide (rust). Rust is formed when iron reacts with the oxygen in the air.

iron + oxygen → iron oxide

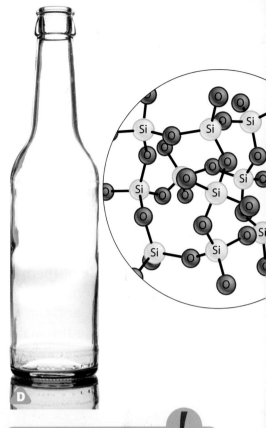

D

4 a How many elements are there in water?
  b Write a word equation for a reaction in which water is formed.
5 Look carefully at diagram D.
  a How many atoms of **i** silicon and **ii** oxygen are shown in the diagram?
  b Why is the formula SiO_2, even though there are far more than three atoms in the diagram?
  c How is silicon dioxide similar to polythene?
  d How is it different?
6 Polythene can burn in oxygen to make carbon dioxide and water.
  a What is the formula of **i** carbon dioxide **ii** water?
  b When you burn polythene, would you get more molecules of carbon dioxide, more water or the same number of molecules of each? Use diagrams to explain your answer.

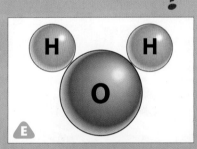

E

Water is an oxide of hydrogen. The word 'hydrogen' means 'water maker', because hydrogen forms water when it burns.

F

H S W

Magnesium is a metal that burns with a bright flame to form an oxide.
o Is magnesium oxide an element or a compound?
o Will the magnesium oxide weigh more or less than the magnesium that you started with? Make a prediction and explain your reasoning.

I CAN...

o explain the words element, compound and molecule.
o use a diagram or chemical formula to work out the name of some simple compounds.
o explain what a chemical formula shows. H S W

How can we make our resources last longer?

If we keep using raw materials and throwing away the products when we finish with them, we may run short of resources. If we use the materials again instead of throwing them away, our use of them becomes more **sustainable**. Many manufacturing processes use a lot of energy, and this can also be reduced if we re-use the materials.

Dumping is No Solution! Go Zero Waste!

A

B

Bottle banks that collect 'clear' glass are using the wrong word! **Clear** means see-through, so almost all glass is clear, although some may be clear green or clear brown. If they were being scientifically accurate, they would say 'colourless'.

Glass

In some countries, whenever you buy anything in a glass bottle, you pay an extra deposit for the bottle. You get the money back if you return the bottle to the shop rather than throwing it away. The bottle can then be washed and **re-used**.

Glass can be recycled if it is crushed up and melted. It can then be made into new bottles. In Britain, the number of green bottles that we use is much greater than the demand for new green glass. Recycled glass can be used in other ways too, such as to make the base material under new roads.

Paper

Paper can be recycled to make brown envelopes, cardboard and toilet paper. Because paper is made from wood, it is a **renewable** resource – if we are careful, we can plant new trees to replace the ones we have chopped down for paper making.

1 Explain the difference between re-use and recycling. H S W

2 Most green bottles that we use are for wine. Suggest why it usually doesn't make sense to re-use wine bottles by sending them back to countries where wine is made, like France and Australia, to be refilled? H S W

Metals

Aluminium is manufactured using a process called **electrolysis**. The process needs a source of aluminium oxide, which is extracted from an ore called **bauxite**. The aluminium oxide then has to be melted and this requires heating to over 1500°C. An electric current is then passed through it and the aluminium oxide splits up like this:

aluminium oxide → aluminium + oxygen

Aluminium metal melts at about 660°C. Using recycled aluminium to make new cans or foil means we don't have to extract and use as much bauxite, and less aluminium is buried in landfill. Recycling also reduces energy costs and carbon dioxide emissions by up to 95%.

c An aluminium factory (note the size of the technician!). Enormous currents (up to 100 000 amps) are used in these factories.

These rulers are made from used vending machine cups.

This chair is made from waste plastics, from household collections.

This mouse mat is made from old plastic bottles.

D

Plastics

It is difficult to re-use plastic bottles. Cleaning the bottles using steam would soften or even melt the plastic. However, most plastics are made from oil, which is running out, so it is important to try to recycle plastics. Most of the black sacks used to collect rubbish will be made of recycled plastics. Recycled plastic can also be used to make products such as traffic cones, crates and even fleeces.

3 In the process of making aluminium, give the name of:
  a a metal element
  b a non-metal element
  c a compound.

4 a Suggest three points in the manufacture of aluminium where energy will be used.
  b Explain how recycling aluminium saves on raw materials and energy. Ⓗ Ⓢ Ⓦ

5 State three uses of recycled plastics.

6 Explain why glass bottles can be re-used but plastic bottles cannot.

7 It has been suggested that we should:
  • make a charge for plastic and paper bags in shops
  • bring back deposits for glass bottles.
  Do you think either of these would be a good idea? Explain your reasons. Ⓗ Ⓢ Ⓦ

I CAN...

o explain the difference between re-using and recycling.
o name some materials that can be recycled.
o explain how recycling can save resources and energy. Ⓗ Ⓢ Ⓦ

8Fe Pay as you throw?

HowScienceworks

Should we charge for non-recyclable rubbish?

Britain has a poor record on recycling compared with many other European countries. One idea is that we could be charged for rubbish collection according to how much waste we throw away. Recycling collections would be free.

A: This sort of measure is vital. We've got to get across the message that we need to reduce waste and recycle more.

E: The council could save on the landfill costs and with the money we raise from the scheme we'd be able to reduce council tax, so many people could be better off.

B: I've got a large family – this could be very expensive for me and I don't know if I could afford it.

F: It's a good idea in principle, but I'm worried that it might mean extra work for those of us who collect the rubbish.

C: We're concerned that some people might try to avoid paying by dumping their rubbish illegally.

G: I pay my taxes already and I reckon the council should just get on with collecting the rubbish without charging us any more – I'm not bothered about any of this recycling business.

D: Well I live on my own and don't make much rubbish, so this plan would suit me.

H: We do now have the technology to fit a computer chip to each bin to measure exactly how much rubbish is being thrown away. We can then charge according to the mass.

HAVE YOUR SAY

Do you think charging people extra for throwing away rubbish is a good idea?

1 Give two arguments in favour and two against the 'Pay as you throw' scheme.

2 Should we be concerned that Britain does not recycle as much as other countries? If you think we should do more, what suggestions would you make for improvement?

Tony Thomson makes jewellery in his workshop in Oxford. He uses a variety of different materials and needs to be sure that they are the finest quality.

> 1 Why do we wear jewellery?
> 2 Name five materials used to make jewellery?

A Jewellers use many different materials.

Most gemstones are **minerals** – substances found in rocks in the Earth's crust. Gemstones like diamonds, rubies and emeralds are very rare minerals. They are hard and attractive and can be cut and polished to reflect the light. Their price depends on their rarity and their quality. Jewellers need to understand a little about chemistry to choose the best materials and spot fake gems.

In the UK precious metals like gold, silver and platinum have a 'hallmark' that shows the quality of the metal. To check hallmarks, chemists are employed to analyse the metals to see what they are made of.

B One of these is a diamond and the other is a rhinestone, a type of glass. Diamonds can be over 1000 times more expensive than rhinestones.

> **!**
> Since the first coins were made over 3000 years ago, people have made fakes. Fakes can be found by looking at the differences in the properties of the metals.

← real roman coin

2000 year old fake →

← modern fake

D

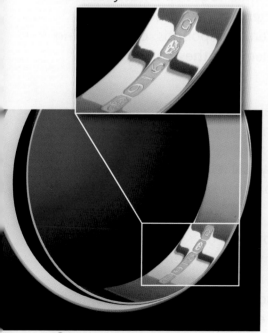

C The hallmark shows us the quality of the metal and when and where it was made.

> 3 a Which stone in photo B do you think is the diamond?
> b Explain your choice.
> 4 a Which coin in photo D do you think is the better fake? Explain your answer.
> b How could a scientist find out which was fake?

How are elements and compounds different?

All the substances around us are made up of tiny particles called **atoms**. The simplest substances are called **elements** and they only contain one kind of atom. Scientists have discovered about 90 natural elements and their names and symbols are listed in the **periodic table** (see page 182).

> In the 1800s, pure aluminium was more expensive than gold. The metal, which is extracted using electricity, was sometimes used to make expensive jewellery and, in 1855, bars of aluminium were exhibited beside the French crown jewels. The price of aluminium has now decreased greatly and it's used to make many useful things, from aeroplanes to cooking foil.

1 Why do you think aluminium is now cheaper than it was 150 years ago? **H S W**

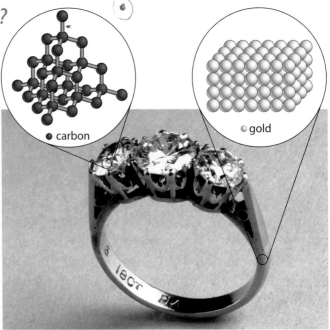

A Some materials used in jewellery are elements, others are compounds.

Compounds contain the atoms of two or more elements joined together by attractions called **bonds**. Scientists have discovered millions of different compounds, often naming them after the elements they contain.

2 Gold is a metal <u>element</u> that is very unreactive so it does not form <u>compounds</u> easily.
  a Explain the meaning of the <u>underlined</u> words.
  b Suggest why gold was among the first elements to be discovered. **H S W**

The **chemical formula** of a substance shows the ratio of atoms of each element that are bonded together. For example the formula of hydrogen chloride is HCl and carbon dioxide is CO_2. In some elements and compounds the atoms are held together in groups called **molecules**. Their formulas show the number of atoms of each element in each molecule.

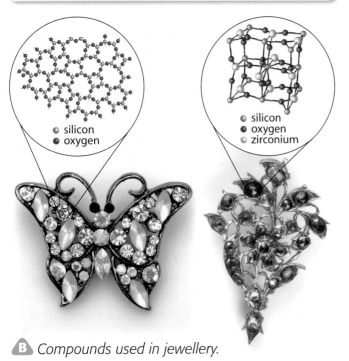

B Compounds used in jewellery.

Substance	Number of atoms joined in a molecule	Chemical name	Chemical formula	Diagram
hydrogen	2 hydrogen	hydrogen	H_2	
water	2 hydrogen 1 oxygen	hydrogen oxide	H_2O	
natural gas	1 carbon 4 hydrogen	carbon hydride	CH_4	
nitric acid	1 hydrogen 1 nitrogen 3 oxygen	hydrogen nitrate	HNO_3	
sulphuric acid	2 hydrogen 1 sulphur 4 oxygen	hydrogen sulphate	H_2SO_4	

C *Some molecules and their formulae.*

3 Look at table C.
  a Which substance is an element?
  b How can you tell?
  c How many elements are joined together in natural gas? 2

  d How many atoms are in each molecule of natural gas?

4 The formula of oxygen is O_2 and ammonia is NH_3. Describe what these formulae tell you about each substance. Ⓗ Ⓢ Ⓦ

Water is an **oxide**. Oxides are compounds that contain oxygen joined to another type of atom. Carbon forms two oxides. Carbon dioxide contains two oxygen atoms for every carbon atom ('di-' means two). Carbon dioxide is the gas produced when fuels burn. The other oxide contains one oxygen atom. This is the deadly gas carbon monoxide ('mono-' means one).

D   carbon dioxide   carbon monoxide

5 a What is the formula of carbon dioxide?
  b Is carbon dioxide an element or a compound?
  c How do you know?

$C\ O_2$

Some molecules have inspired jewellery.

E

I CAN...

o explain the difference between atoms and molecules.
o recognise examples of elements and compounds.
o explain what a chemical formula tells you about a substance.   Ⓗ Ⓢ Ⓦ

How are compounds different from their elements?

Iron pyrite is a compound of two elements, iron and sulphur. These are both solid elements. Iron is magnetic, but sulphur is not. Photo B shows the elements in powder form. There is also a mixture of iron and sulphur. The elements in the mixture are not combined together. If you pass a magnet over the mixture, only the iron is attracted towards the magnet. The sulphur stays on the dish.

A Iron pyrite or fool's gold.

B Mixtures of iron and sulphur can be separated easily.

1 Describe the appearance of the:
   a iron   b sulphur.
2 a Which of the elements is a metal?
   b Name one special property of this metal.
3 How can you tell that the elements do not form a compound when you just mix them? Ⓗ Ⓢ Ⓦ

Iron and sulphur react together when heated. The atoms of iron and sulphur join together to form a compound called iron sulphide. Once the reaction has started, you can take the tube out of the flame, and it will carry on glowing. Energy is usually released when the atoms **bond** together and this energy is given out into the surroundings.

When the reaction is over, the iron and sulphur are bonded strongly together and form a single solid compound. The iron sulphide is very different from the elements that it is made up from.

The word equation for the reaction is:

iron + sulphur → iron sulphide

In 1576 the pirate and explorer Martin Frobisher (1535–1594) formed a company backed by Queen Elizabeth I to bring back 2300 tons of a black rock containing a golden substance from Canada to England. The queen ordered the rocks to be stored in the Tower of London and the company expected to make a fortune. Unfortunately the rocks only contained iron pyrite or fool's gold and the investors, including the queen, lost all their money.

C The chemical reaction gives out heat and the mixture glows red.

D You cannot separate the elements in iron sulphide with a magnet.

4 How do you know a reaction has started, when the iron and sulphur mixture is heated?

5 Give one piece of evidence that suggests that iron sulphide is a different substance from:
a iron   **b** sulphur.   Ⓗ Ⓢ Ⓦ

The atoms in iron sulphide do not join together in simple molecules. In this compound the atoms are arranged to form a large regular pattern. The formula of iron sulphide is FeS. This means that for every iron atom in the solid there is one sulphur atom. The formula shows us that the ratio of iron atoms to sulphur atoms is 1:1.

Quartz and rhinestones are different forms of the compound silicon dioxide, which always has the same formula SiO_2. This means that the silicon dioxide in rhinestones has the same ratio of silicon and oxygen atoms as the silicon dioxide in quartz. A chemical compound always contains the same elements in the same ratio. If the ratio changes, it means that you have got a different chemical compound.

!

Scientists have now produced synthetic diamonds that are better than rhinestones. One of the best is made from a very rare mineral called moissanite. This is only found naturally in meteorites that came from outside our Solar System. Moissanite is a form of silicon carbide and has the formula SiC.

6 Describe how silicon oxide is different from its elements.   Ⓗ Ⓢ Ⓦ

7 Magnesium oxide is a solid with the formula MgO.
a Draw a particle diagram to show the arrangement of atoms in solid magnesium oxide. Show at least 12 atoms.   Ⓗ Ⓢ Ⓦ
b Write a word equation for the formation of magnesium oxide from its elements.   Ⓗ Ⓢ Ⓦ

Ⓗ Ⓢ Ⓦ

What other tests might you carry out to show that iron sulphide is different from its elements?

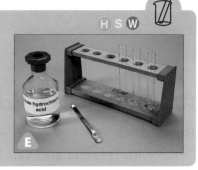
E

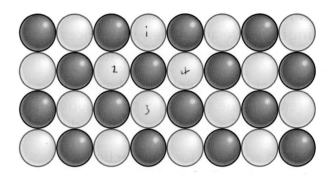
F *The arrangement of atoms in iron sulphide.*

G *Quartz and rhinestones are different forms of silicon dioxide.*

I CAN...

○ describe the changes you might see happening, when compounds are formed from their elements.

○ use evidence to describe how compounds are different from their elements.   Ⓗ Ⓢ Ⓦ

○ identify elements and compounds from particle diagrams.   Ⓗ Ⓢ Ⓦ

What different types of change can occur?

Heat can be used to bring about change. When jewellers heat gold, it melts and can be moulded into different shapes. The liquid metal easily turns back into a solid as it cools. All changes of state, like melting and evaporation, are **physical changes**. There are no new substances formed and often it is easy to reverse a physical change.

If fool's gold, iron sulphide, is heated in air or oxygen, a different change occurs. Two new substances are formed: solid iron oxide and a poisonous gas called sulphur dioxide.

The word equation for this reaction is:

iron sulphide + oxygen → iron oxide + sulphur dioxide

A Heat can cause physical changes in substances.

This is a **chemical change** as new substances are formed and it would be difficult to change these **products** back into the **reactants**.

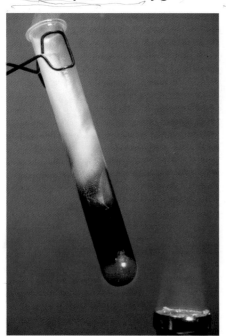

B Heat can cause a chemical change.

1 What two products are formed when iron sulphide is heated in air?
2 What is meant by:
   a reactants   b products?
3 Give three examples of physical changes.
4 Describe how heat can be used to tell real gold from fool's gold.   Ⓗ Ⓢ Ⓦ

!

Chemical reactions can be used to test for materials and spot fakes. If concentrated acid is added to gold, no reaction occurs. If the acid is added to fool's gold (iron sulphide) a gas called hydrogen sulphide is produced. This is the same gas that puts the stink into stink bombs!

Malachite is a green stone that can be used in jewellery when polished. Malachite is mainly copper carbonate, and if it is heated strongly it turns black and a gas is given off. The malachite has **decomposed** (broken apart) and carbon dioxide gas and copper oxide have been formed.

The word equation for this reaction is:

copper carbonate → copper oxide + carbon dioxide

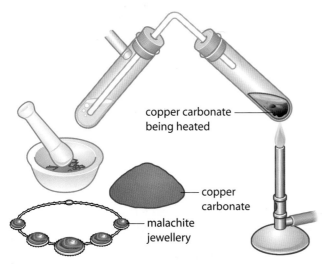

copper carbonate being heated

copper carbonate

malachite jewellery

C The limewater turns milky showing carbon dioxide is produced.

Some chemical reactions occur without heating. As soon as sodium carbonate and copper sulphate solutions are mixed, a green solid is formed. The green solid is called a precipitate and in this reaction it is copper carbonate. A solution of sodium sulphate is also formed. This is an example of a **precipitation** reaction.

sodium carbonate + **copper sulphate** → **copper carbonate** + **sodium sulphate**

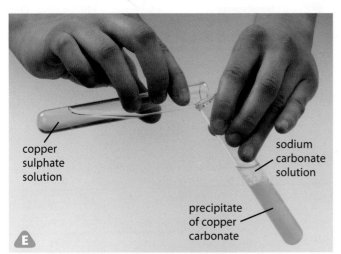

copper sulphate solution

sodium carbonate solution

precipitate of copper carbonate

E

7 How do we know a chemical reaction has happened?

8 When lead nitrate solution is added to sodium iodide solution solid lead iodide is formed.
  a Write a word equation for this reaction. (H)(S)(W)
  b What is this type of reaction called?

5 Look at diagram C.
  a How can you tell that a chemical reaction has occurred?
  b What colour is copper oxide? (H)(S)(W)

6 Lead carbonate reacts in a similar way to copper carbonate when heated.
  a Write a word equation for this reaction. (H)(S)(W)
  b How could you show that carbon dioxide was given off? (H)(S)(W)

H S W

D

When you mix chemicals together, or heat them, how can you tell if a chemical reaction has taken place?
  ○ How will you record your observations?
  ○ Which observations provide the best evidence?

I CAN...

  ○ explain the difference between physical changes and chemical reactions and give examples.
  ○ explain that some reactions need heat to start them off.
  ○ explain what precipitation and decomposition reactions are.
  ○ write word equations for chemical changes and name reactants and products. H S W

8Gc Pure dead brilliant

How are mixtures different from elements and compounds?

The elements and compounds we use every day are hardly ever found on their own. They are nearly always found mixed together with other substances. Air, rocks, soil and natural water are all mixtures. **Mixtures** are much more common than **pure** substances.

> **1 a** Thinking about things found around us, name four mixtures.
> **b** Choose one and describe what is in the mixture.

Pure water is a compound made from the elements hydrogen and oxygen. In the compound, the atoms of hydrogen and oxygen are joined together.

A Many different mixtures of metals and minerals are used to make jewellery.

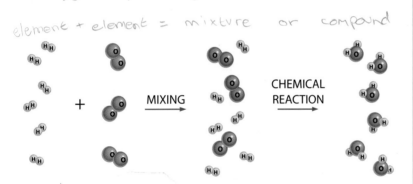

element + element = mixture or compound

+ MIXING CHEMICAL REACTION

B Elements, mixtures and compounds.

	Volvic (mg/litre)	Highland Spring (mg/litre)	Malvern (mg/litre)
calcium	10	35	35
magnesium	6	9	15
sodium	9	6	15
potassium	6	1	1
bicarbonate	65	136	123
chloride	8	8	39
sulphate	7	6	35
nitrate	6	0	8

C Different substances found in mineral waters.

A pure substance contains only one element or compound. Not all water is pure. The water in seas and oceans and even the water we drink contains other substances. They are all mixtures. Seawater is 'salty' as it contains different soluble compounds, including sodium chloride. Even our clean drinking water contains chemicals that have dissolved from the rocks it flowed over. Water from different areas contains different amounts of chemicals and can taste different.

● How could you show that water contains dissolved chemicals?
● How could you find the mass of dissolved salts in water?

> **2** What is the difference between pure water and clean water?
> **3** Why can't we say that our drinking water is pure?

4 Draw up a table with three columns headed element, compound and mixture. Put these substances in the correct column:

air   carbon dioxide   gold   iron sulphide   oxygen
silicon dioxide   silver   soap powder   soil

A particular compound always contains the same elements in the same ratio. Mixtures are different; there can be different amounts of chemicals in a mixture. The chemicals in a mixture are not joined to each other, they are simply jumbled up together. For example, air is a mixture of gases. Air we breathe out contains more carbon dioxide than the air we breathe in. Warm air can contain more water vapour than cold air. We can represent compounds and elements by formulae, but we cannot use formulae for mixtures.

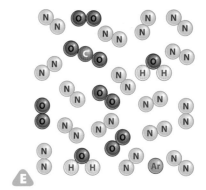

E

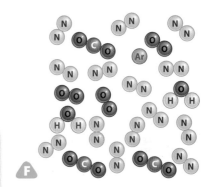

F

5 Give the name of the gas in air which:
  a is a compound
  b is an element with more than one atom in a molecule
  c is made up of molecules that contain three atoms.
6 Look at diagrams E and F. Which drawing shows breathed out air? Explain your answer.
7 There is no formula for seawater. Why not?   Ⓗ Ⓢ Ⓦ

Natural gas, the fuel used in Bunsen burners, is mainly methane. However, it also contains small amounts of other gases, including ethane and some gases from air. The chemical formula for methane is CH_4.

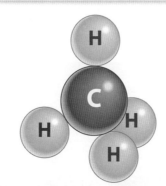

G *A methane molecule.*

Ⓗ Ⓢ Ⓦ ❗

Methane gas can be dangerous because it has no smell. A compound called methyl mercaptan (formula CH_3SH) is usually mixed with natural gas, so that leaks can be detected. Methyl mercaptan smells of rotten eggs and is also responsible for the smell of bad breath and animal manure.

8 a Name three chemicals in natural gas.
  b Is natural gas an element, mixture or compound? Explain your answer.
  c Is methane an element, mixture or compound? Explain your answer.
  d In a molecule of methane, how many:
    i atoms are there
    ii elements are there?

I CAN...

○ explain the difference between a mixture and a compound.
○ explain what is meant by a pure substance.
○ recognise elements, compounds and mixtures from particle diagrams.   Ⓗ Ⓢ Ⓦ

What makes gold so special?

Gold is an excellent choice for making jewellery as it has special properties. It is **unreactive**, shiny when polished and easy to bend and shape. Pure gold is too soft for many uses but mixing it with other metals like copper, nickel, silver or platinum makes it stronger and more hardwearing. Mixtures of metals are called **alloys**. Most jewellery is made with an alloy of gold.

The properties of an alloy depend on the type and amounts of each metal in the mixture. Different alloys are made for different uses. Some alloys have to be **ductile** so they can be drawn into wires and others have to be **malleable** so they can be hammered into shape.

The great philosopher and mathematician Archimedes (287–212 BCE) is probably most famous for running down the street naked shouting 'Eureka' on discovering that a solid will displace its own volume of water. The idea came to him as he stepped into a full bath and he later used the idea to prove that a pure gold crown of King Hieron II was a fake. He did this by comparing the volume of water displaced by the crown and an equal mass of pure gold. The crown displaced more water showing that it contained lighter metal than gold.

A Different gold alloys.

The original system measured the purity of gold objects in carats. One carat is 1 part in 24. So pure gold is 24 carats and 12 carat gold contains 50% gold.

The newer 'fineness' or 'millesimal' system measures purity in parts per thousand. In this system, pure gold is 1000 and an object made of 50% gold is 500.

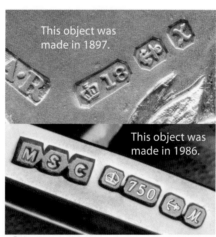

This object was made in 1897.

This object was made in 1986.

B The purity of gold is included in its hallmark.

1 What is an alloy?
2 Choose two properties of gold and explain why they are useful in making jewellery.
3 Why is pure gold not used for jewellery?
4 Look at photo A. Explain how the properties of each alloy are different to pure gold.

I CAN...

o explain what an alloy is and why they are used.
o calculate the purity of gold from suitable information.

5 a Which system for measuring gold do you think is better?
  b Can you think of another way of measuring purity?

How can electricity be used to make jewellery? HowScienceWorks

Electricity can be used to decompose some compounds that cannot be broken down by heat. This process is called **electrolysis**. The electrical energy breaks the bonds that hold the atoms together. The elements are separated from each other and collect at each **electrode**. Photograph A shows the electrolysis of copper chloride solution.

Electrolysis only works if the compounds are molten or in solution. In general, a metal forms at the negative electrode and a non-metal forms at the positive electrode.

Scientists have found ways of using electrolysis to put a thin coating of one metal onto the surface of another metal. The process is called **electroplating** and it is used in several different industries.

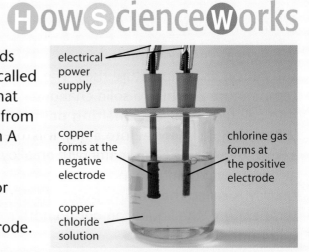

electrical power supply

copper forms at the negative electrode

chlorine gas forms at the positive electrode

copper chloride solution

A Copper metal collects at the negative electrode while bubbles of chlorine gas are produced at the positive electrode.

B Electroplated gold and silver, as shown here, can look as good as the real thing and is much cheaper to use. However, the coating is thin and can wear away in time.

1 Photo A shows copper chloride being decomposed using electricity.
   a What word describes this process?
   b Which two elements are produced?
   c Where is the metal formed?

!
Electricity is used to deposit a thin layer of gold on the plugs of headphones. This reduces the electrical resistance of the contact and improves the sound quality. The layer of metal used in electroplating is about 0.001 mm thick!

2 Which elements would you get when electricity is passed through molten lead bromide?.
3 Describe one advantage and one disadvantage of electroplated gold jewellery.
4 Draw a labelled diagram to show how a piece of copper jewellery can be electroplated with silver. Your diagram should include: power supply, silver nitrate solution, silver rod and jewellery.

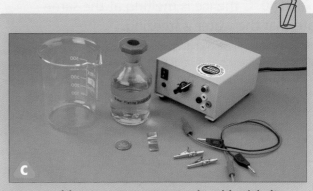

C

How could you coat a copper coin with nickel?

8Ge Melt it down

How can melting and boiling points help to tell us if something is fake?

When heat energy is put in to a substance, its temperature rises. The temperature at which a solid changes into a liquid is called its **melting point**. When a liquid changes into a gas, it is said to **evaporate**. The temperature at which evaporation happens most quickly is called the **boiling point**. At this temperature, the liquid can get no hotter (although the gas can).

1 What is the melting point of platinum?
2 At what temperature will ethanol turn into a gas very quickly?
3 Name a liquid that will boil in your freezer.
4 The melting point of diamond was calculated. Suggest why scientists have never found the melting point by experiment. Ⓗ Ⓢ Ⓦ

The melting point of a substance is also its **freezing point**. At precisely 0 °C *pure* water will be an equal mixture of water and ice. Slightly above this temperature and all the ice will become liquid, slightly below it and all the liquid water will become ice. At exactly 0 °C the ice is melting at the same rate that the water is freezing.

5 Do you think that boiling points are always higher than melting points? Explain your reasoning. Ⓗ Ⓢ Ⓦ
6 What is the freezing point of:
    a water b platinum?

Platinum is often used to make jewellery. The melting point of platinum is 1772 °C.

The melting point of diamond is 3550 °C, the highest of any known material.

Liquid nitrogen melts at −210 °C and boils at −196 °C.
Ⓐ

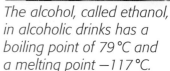

The alcohol, called ethanol, in alcoholic drinks has a boiling point of 79 °C and a melting point −117 °C.

Chocolate is made with a melting point of 36 °C. This is just below body temperature, so the chocolate will melt in the mouth.

Pure elements and pure compounds have precise melting and boiling points. Mixtures do not. They melt and boil over a range of temperatures. For example, pure gold melts at 1063°C, but 18 carat gold melts somewhere between 895 and 930°C. Eighteen carat gold is an alloy of gold mixed with copper and silver. This means that the melting point of a substance can be used to tell us if it is pure or not.

The melting points and boiling points of all substances are affected by impurities. Pure water melts at 0°C. Impurities in the water can change the melting and boiling points. Adding salt to water lowers its melting point.

B Salt is spread on the roads in the winter so the water does not freeze so easily.

7 Why is salt spread on the roads in winter? **H S W**

8 Why do ice lollies need to be kept well below the freezing point of water?

9 Science books often list the melting and boiling points of substances. However, the melting and boiling points of air are never given. Why not?

H S W

The Kelvin temperature scale (symbol K) was developed by Lord Kelvin (1824–1907) in 1848. The zero point in this scale is −273.16°C, which is the lowest temperature possible. The boiling point of water in the Kelvin scale is 373°K.

Solder is an alloy made by mixing tin (melting point 232°C) and lead (melting point 328°C). The mixture of tin and lead melts at a lower temperature than either of the two metals when they are pure.

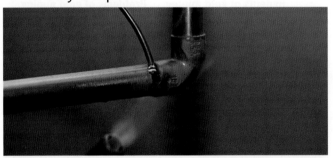

C Solder melts easily to join copper pipes.

H S W

How would you find out if adding salt to water changes its boiling point?
- Does it matter how much salt you use?
- How would you make sure your results are fair and reliable?

D

10 Why can solder be more useful than pure lead or tin?

11 How do you think antifreeze affects the freezing point of water? **H S W**

12 Samples from two different silver coins were taken. Silver coin X melted at exactly 962°C. Silver coin Y melted between 951°C and 959°C.
   a Which coin was made of pure silver?
   b Explain your answer to **a**.
   c Why is this *not* a good method to use to discover fakes? **H S W**

I CAN...

- explain what melting, freezing and boiling points are.
- explain the effect of impurities on the melting and boiling points of substances.
- use melting and boiling point data to decide if a substance is pure. **H S W**

Is our jewellery really worth it?

Gold mining is vital for many developing countries as it provides income for the economy, work and training for the population and introduces new technologies. Gold mining can also bring about improvements to transport systems and essential services like water and electricity supplies. Over 85% of the gold mined is sold to the more wealthy countries, where it is used to make jewellery. Unfortunately there are hidden costs in the production of gold that are not reflected in its price.

1 Why should gold mining operations in a country improve:
   a transport links?   b electricity supplies?
2 What fraction of the gold produced is *not* used to make jewellery?

B *A digger is used to search for gold miners trapped by a landslide at a mine in Colombia.*

! It is estimated that at least 2.8 tons of rock and earth are excavated to mine the gold needed to make one wedding ring.

HowScienceWorks

A *What do we drink?*

3 a What compound is commonly used to extract gold?
   b What problem does its use cause?
4 Why does gold mining produce so much waste?
5 What are the benefits and problems of gold mining in a developing country? Write down your ideas in a table like the one below.

Benefits of gold mining	Problems of gold mining

C *Gold mining can help bring about improvements in water supplies but is this a good use of an essential resource?*

HAVE YOUR SAY

Some people think that the mining of gold in developing countries exploits workers. Do you think that we should stop buying jewellery that is made with new gold?

8Ha Explaining the Earth

HowScienceWorks

The surface of the Earth is made of many different kinds of rocks. It is shaped by **weathering** and **erosion**, but also by more dramatic events such as erupting **volcanoes** and **earthquakes**.

Geologists study the Earth to find out how the different kinds of rock were formed. They also find out why we have volcanoes and earthquakes, and try to predict when these will happen. Geologists collaborate with other scientists to investigate how organisms and the Earth's **climate** have changed over millions of years.

In many areas of science, the first step in studying many different things is to see if they can be **classified**. *Geologists like Anna classify rocks into three main groups according to their* **texture**: *sedimentary*, *igneous* and *metamorphic*.

A *Soldiers searching for earthquake victims in China in May, 2008. The earthquake killed around 70 000 people.*

B

C *This cliff is made from* **gneiss**.

D *The Giant's Causeway is made from* **basalt**.

E *The rocks in the sides of the Grand Canyon are mostly* **limestone** *and* **sandstone**.

1 Why do you think it is important to study the Earth? Give as many different reasons as you can.

2 a How can rocks be weathered? Describe as many different kinds of weathering as you can.

 b Erosion is when broken up bits of rock are moved. Describe four different ways in which this can happen.

3 Suggest why it is useful to classify objects when studying them.

4 a Look at the rocks in photos C, D and E. Which group does each rock belong in?

 b What are the characteristics of the three groups of rocks?

●●● **105**

How are sedimentary rocks formed?

Rocks are made up of **grains**. Each grain is usually made from one **mineral**. Different rocks contain different mixtures of minerals. Rocks can be broken up by **chemical weathering**, **physical weathering** or **biological weathering**.

A *A limestone pavement.*

1 Look at photos A and B carefully. In which photo can you see examples of: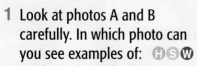
   a physical weathering
   b chemical weathering?
   c Explain your reasoning.
2 Describe one way in which biological weathering can break up rocks.

B *Rocks at the top of Glyder Fach in Wales.*

When rock is weathered, pieces may fall from the rock face or be washed away by water. This is called **erosion**. These fragments of rock (**sediments**) can be **transported** by moving water, wind or ice. When the water or wind slows down, or the ice melts, the fragments are **deposited** as layers of sediment.

Over a long period of time, more layers of sediment are deposited on top of the first one. As this happens, the newer layers on top squash the bottom layers. The pressure from these newer layers forces the grains of sediment closer together. This squashing (called compaction) squeezes the water out from between the grains.

The grains of sediments have gaps between them. Water can flow through these gaps. If the water contains dissolved minerals, the minerals can form **crystals** in the gaps. The crystals act as a 'glue' that **cements** the grains together. **Compaction** and **cementation** together change sediments into sedimentary rocks.

3 How is sedimentary rock made from a layer of sediment?
4 Would the oldest sedimentary rocks be at the top or the bottom of a cliff? Explain your answer.
5 Where does the glue come from that holds the grains together in a sedimentary rock?

Sedimentary rocks contain evidence that can tell us about the conditions in which they were formed. For example, the size of the grains can tell us how fast the water was flowing that moved them.

!

The oldest sedimentary rocks in the UK are around 1000 million years old.

C Suilven in Scotland is made of thick layers of sandstone with large grains, and bands of pebbles. The sediments were deposited by rivers that flooded across the land about 1000 million years ago.

 H S W

Examine some samples of sedimentary rocks.
- What characteristics do they all have in common?
- What are the differences between them?
- What does each rock tell you about the way it was formed?

6 What evidence is there in the rocks in Suilven to show how the sediments were deposited? H S W

7 a Describe how limestone and chalk are formed.

  b Explain why limestone is evidence that the land was once under a warm, shallow sea. H S W

D The **chalk** and **limestone** cliffs along the south coast of England are made from the shells of sea creatures. They show that this part of the country was once covered in warm, shallow seas.

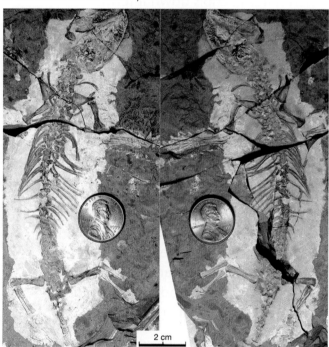

2 cm

E **Fossils** found in sedimentary rocks can tell us what living organisms were like in the past. This fossil of a mammal that lived 125 million years ago was found in China in 2007.

I CAN...

- describe how sedimentary rocks are formed.
- use evidence from sedimentary rocks to explain how they were formed. H S W

How are igneous rocks formed?

The solid rocks we live on are called the **crust** of the Earth. Underneath the crust is a layer called the **mantle**. The Earth is very hot inside. Sometimes the mantle and crust become so hot that they melt. The molten rock is called **magma**.

> 1 What is magma?

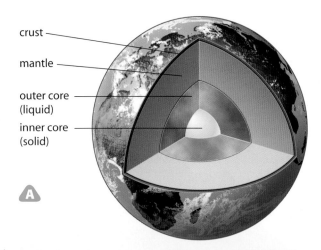

crust
mantle
outer core (liquid)
inner core (solid)

A

When magma cools down it forms **igneous** rocks. Igneous rocks can look very different from each other. If magma cools down fast, it forms rocks containing small crystals, such as **basalt**. This can happen when magma flows out of the Earth's crust in a volcano. Magma that reaches the Earth's surface is called **lava**. Lava cools quickly in the air or underwater.

Magma can be trapped underground. Large volumes of magma will cool very slowly and form rocks containing large crystals, such as **granite**. If the magma has been forced into narrow gaps in existing rocks it can cool quickly and form rocks with small crystals.

Magma or lava can contain different combinations of chemicals. The kind of rock that is formed depends on the chemicals in the magma (or lava) and on how fast it cools.

> 2 What is the difference between lava and magma?
> 3 a How is granite formed?
>   b How could you tell this by looking at a lump of granite? Ⓗ Ⓢ Ⓦ

B *This lava is cooling quickly on the surface of the Earth.*

sedimentary rock

igneous rock

sedimentary rock

C *The igneous rock was formed when magma was forced into the existing sedimentary rock and cooled.*

We can explain the difference in the crystal sizes by thinking about what happens to the **particles** in melted rock. When the rock is a liquid, the particles are free to move about. As the liquid cools down, **bonds** form between the particles. The bonds stick the particles together. As more bonds form, the particles become fixed in their positions. The particles are completely fixed in place when the crystals are solid.

If the rock cools down slowly, there will be time for lots of particles to move and stick together (bond) in an ordered arrangement, making large crystals. If the rock cools down quickly, there will only be time for a few particles to bond in an ordered arrangement, so smaller crystals will be made.

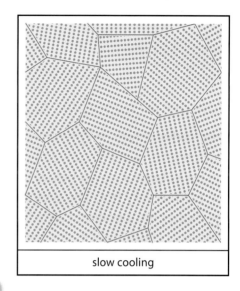

slow cooling

4 a Why can particles move in melted rock? (H)(S)(W)
  b What happens to the particles as the liquid rock starts to cool down? (H)(S)(W)
  c Why do some rocks have bigger crystals than others? (H)(S)(W)
5 Why does magma usually cool more slowly than lava?
6 Look at photo C. Do you think the igneous rock in photo C will have large or small crystals? Explain your answer. (H)(S)(W)

fast cooling

(H)(S)(W)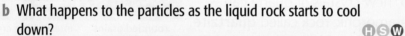

A TV company wants to make a programme to show how the sizes of granite crystals are different depending on how fast they have cooled. They can't use granite because it is too difficult to melt. How could they demonstrate this using another chemical?

o Should the chemical that they use have a higher or lower melting point than granite?

E

I CAN...

o describe how igneous rocks are formed.
o explain how the size of crystals is evidence for the speed of cooling.

H S (W)

How are metamorphic rocks formed?

After sedimentary or igneous rocks are formed, they may get compressed by earth movements. The earth movements may force the rocks further down below the surface of the Earth. The inside of the Earth is very hot. The pressure from the earth movements and the higher temperature cause the rock to change. Rocks formed by changing existing rocks are called **metamorphic** rocks. When a rock changes, the properties of the rock change as well.

Sandstones are made mostly from a mineral called **quartz**. If sandstone is heated and compressed, new crystals of quartz can grow. The sandstone turns into a metamorphic rock called **quartzite**. The quartzite consists of interlocking crystals, which make it much harder than the sandstone from which it was formed.

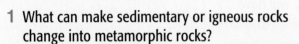

sandstone → quartzite

rounded grains   interlocking crystals

A

1 What can make sedimentary or igneous rocks change into metamorphic rocks?

2 What happens to the minerals in sandstone when it changes into quartzite?

3 Suggest why sandstone is porous but quartzite is not.

limestone   marble

B Limestone is a sedimentary rock. **Marble** is a metamorphic rock formed when limestone is heated and compressed.

!

Gneiss is a metamorphic rock made from **mudstone**. The oldest rocks in the UK are gneiss rocks in north-west Scotland. They are about 3000 million years old.

C

4 Name two sedimentary rocks and the metamorphic rocks they change into.

5 Which would be easier to carve into a statue – a sedimentary or a metamorphic rock? Explain your answer.

Most rocks are made of mixtures of different minerals. When rocks like this are heated and compressed, the minerals in the rock react to form different minerals. Some minerals naturally form long crystals, and these are usually lined up in metamorphic rocks. Sometimes the new minerals form thick, coloured bands. The amount of change depends on the temperatures and pressures on the rocks.

increasing temperature and pressure when metamorphic rock was formed →

Mudstone is a soft, sedimentary rock.

Slate can be split into thin layers, because the crystals are lined up in the same direction. It is much harder than mudstone.

Schist often looks shiny because flakes of a mineral called mica are lined up.

Gneiss (pronounced 'nice') usually has bands of different coloured minerals.

increasing thickness of layers   increasing crystal size →

D *Mudstone can turn into slate, schist or gneiss, depending on how high the temperature and pressure gets.*

Metamorphic rocks can also be formed around magma in the Earth's crust. The heat from the magma changes the rocks around it.

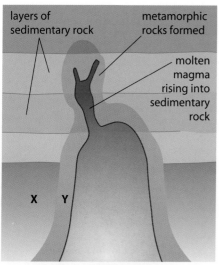

layers of sedimentary rock

metamorphic rocks formed

molten magma rising into sedimentary rock

X   Y

E

6 Give an example of a heat source that can form metamorphic rocks.

7 Describe what evidence you would look for to decide if a rock was sedimentary, igneous or metamorphic. Ⓗ Ⓢ Ⓦ

8 Look at diagram E. Rock Y is marble. What kind of rock do you think is found at X? Explain your answer.

 Ⓗ Ⓢ Ⓦ

How would you examine the differences between a metamorphic rock and the sedimentary rock from which it was made? Investigate several pairs of rocks.

● Do you find the same differences for all your pairs of rocks?

I CAN...

○ recall the names of some metamorphic rocks and the rocks from which they were formed.

○ describe how metamorphic rocks are formed.

○ describe the evidence used to distinguish metamorphic rocks from sedimentary or igneous rocks. Ⓗ Ⓢ Ⓦ

How is the history of the Earth explained by different theories?

How**S**cience**w**orks

There have been many different ideas to explain the history of the Earth and how the mountains and other features formed. Before people started to make scientific observations and theories, many cultures invented creation myths to explain how the Earth was formed.

A scientific **theory** is an idea that can explain observations, and can be used to make predictions that can be tested. If the predictions are correct, the theory is accepted by scientists. If they are not, the theory is changed or abandoned.

Creationism

Many religions have ancient texts that claim that the Earth was created by a god (or gods) in a period of a few days, or in a few thousand years. If you wanted to test this idea, you would predict that all the rocks on the Earth would be about the same age. Scientists have many different ways of working out how old rocks are, and have found that the ages of rocks range from less than a year old to 3800 million years. Most scientists do not believe creation theories.

A A Chinese legend says that Pangu emerged from an egg and separated the Earth from the sky. This took 18 000 years.

> 1 What is a scientific theory?
> 2 Why is Creationism not usually regarded as a scientific theory today?

Catastrophism

The catastrophe theory suggested that the shape of the surface of the Earth was formed by a series of sudden catastrophes. According to the supporters of this theory, such as Peter Pallas (1741–1811) and Jean Baptiste de Beaumont (1798–1874), these catastrophes were violent events, like huge earthquakes, floods or volcanic eruptions, which changed the landscape of the Earth.

B A volcanic eruption formed a new island, called Surtsey, in 1963. Surtsey is near Iceland.

Uniformitarianism

This theory about the Earth was developed by James Hutton (1726–1797). He suggested that we might be able to find out about the origin of ancient rocks by studying 'present-day' events such as weathering, transportation and sedimentation. He thought that the same processes had been occurring since the Earth was formed. Hutton was the first person to consider that changes in our landscape take many thousands or millions of years to happen – 'geological time' is very long.

Charles Lyell (1797–1875) developed Hutton's ideas and gathered more evidence for them. He presented the idea of uniformitarianism in his book, *Principles of Geology*. These ideas were widely accepted by scientists.

> **3** What do you think is meant by 'geological time'?
>
> **4 a** What is the main difference between the theories of uniformitarianism and catastrophism?
>
> **b** Which of these theories is most likely to be supported by people who think that the Bible is literally true? Explain your answer.

Modern ideas

Geologists today accept that uniformitarianism is basically correct, but that there *are* catastrophic events as well that shape the Earth.

D **Meteorites** or **comets** have struck the Earth many times in the past, and could do so again. This crater was formed about 50 000 years ago. Scientists think the meteorite was about 40 m in diameter.

> **5** Suggest why people no longer think that catastrophism can explain all Earth processes.

C *An illustration from Lyell's book, showing the Temple of Serapios in Italy. Lyell used evidence on the pillars to show that the level of the sea had changed several times over hundreds of years.*

I CAN...

o describe some different theories that have been suggested to explain how rocks formed.

o explain why these theories were accepted or rejected.

What happens on the Earth's surface?

HowScienceWorks

Alfred Wegener (1880–1930) published a book in 1915 in which he suggested that the continents moved around slowly on the surface of the Earth. This theory was known as **continental drift**. This idea suggested that mountains were formed when continents crashed into each other. He was not the first to suggest this idea, but he was the first to provide a lot of detailed evidence to back up his theory.

Most scientists at the time did not accept Wegener's ideas. Some of the reasons for this were:

• Wegener could not explain how the continents could move through the rocks on the sea beds.

• There were other explanations for the similar fossils in Africa and South America, such as land bridges that allowed animals to travel from one continent to another.

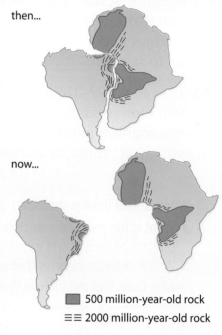

then...

now...

■ 500 million-year-old rock
≡≡ 2000 million-year-old rock

A Some of Wegener's evidence for his theory of continental drift. The shapes of Africa and South America seem to fit together, and rocks on each side of the Atlantic Ocean match up. Similar fossils of land animals are also found on both sides of the Atlantic.

---

1 a What was the theory of continental drift?
  b How did the theory explain how mountains were formed?
2 Why wasn't Wegener's idea accepted by most scientists?

Geologists continued to investigate the Earth and to make new observations. These included mapping the sea floor. In 1962, Harry Hess (1906–1969) proposed the theory of **plate tectonics**.

This theory suggested that the surface of the Earth is split into several **plates**, which move around slowly, driven by **convection currents** in the mantle. This theory had the ocean floors moving *with* the continents, rather than Wegener's idea of the continents ploughing *through* the ocean floors.

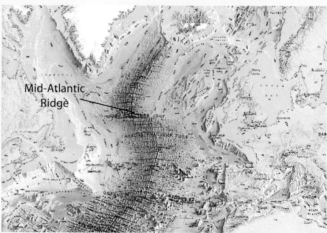

Mid-Atlantic Ridge

B Mapping the sea floor showed that most oceans had a line of mountains up the middle. This map shows what lies beneath the Atlantic Ocean.

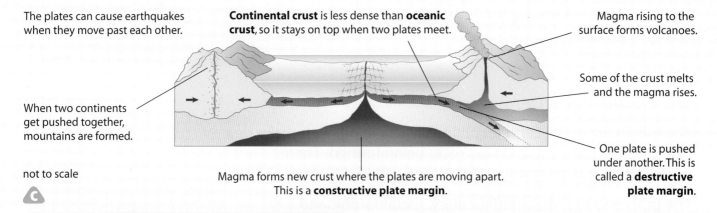

The plates can cause earthquakes when they move past each other.

Continental crust is less dense than **oceanic crust**, so it stays on top when two plates meet.

Magma rising to the surface forms volcanoes.

When two continents get pushed together, mountains are formed.

Some of the crust melts and the magma rises.

One plate is pushed under another. This is called a **destructive plate margin**.

not to scale

Magma forms new crust where the plates are moving apart. This is a **constructive plate margin**.

C

3 What is a plate?

4 What is a constructive plate margin?

5 What is a destructive plate margin?

Geologists have been continuing to study the Earth. The details of this theory have been modified slightly since Hess first proposed it to take account of new evidence. Plate tectonics is the currently accepted theory that explains how the Earth works. It can explain many observations, such as:

• why volcanoes and earthquakes occur only in particular parts of the world, as shown in map D

• why there are mountain ridges beneath the oceans

• why the rocks on the ocean floors are usually much younger than the rocks in the continents

• why sediments on the ocean floors are much thicker nearer to the edges of the oceans than they are at the centre.

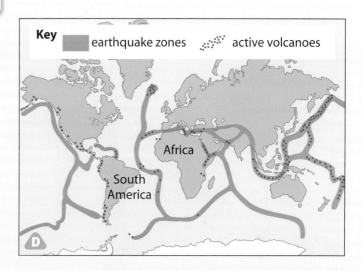

Key ▢ earthquake zones ⋰ active volcanoes

Africa

South America

D

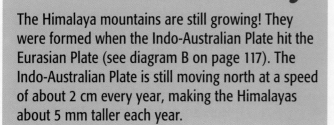

!

The Himalaya mountains are still growing! They were formed when the Indo-Australian Plate hit the Eurasian Plate (see diagram B on page 117). The Indo-Australian Plate is still moving north at a speed of about 2 cm every year, making the Himalayas about 5 mm taller each year.

6 Look at map D, and at map B on page 117. Suggest why volcanoes and earthquakes only occur in certain places.

7 Look at diagram C.
  a Where are the newest rocks in the ocean floor?
  b Why are sediments thicker nearer to the edges of oceans?

8 a What happens to the oceanic crust when it meets continental crust?
  b Why is oceanic crust usually much younger than continental crust?

9 Why do you think scientists accept the theory of plate tectonics rather than Wegener's theory of continental drift?

What is the rock cycle?

The outer part of the Earth is continually changing, with rocks being weathered away and new rocks being formed. These processes have been going on since the Earth was formed.

The processes that make sedimentary, metamorphic and igneous rocks are linked together, forming a cycle that is never ending. Some processes in the **rock cycle** are quick, but most are so slow that we do not notice that they are happening.

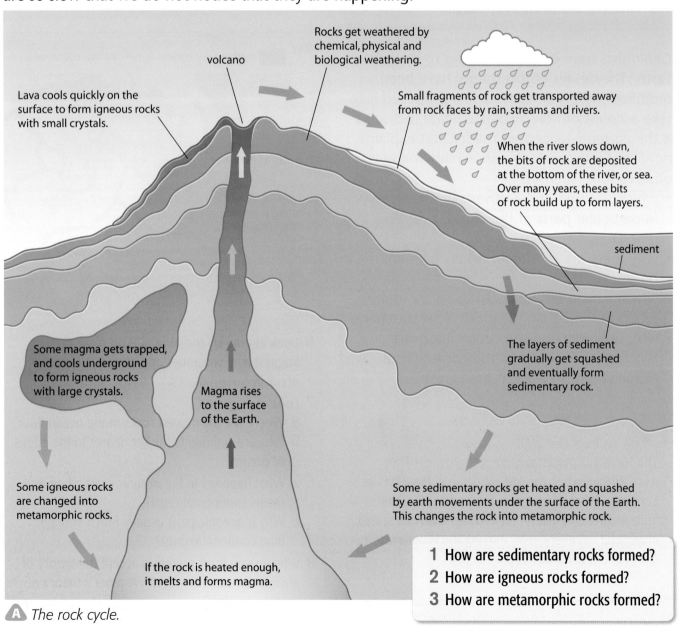

Lava cools quickly on the surface to form igneous rocks with small crystals.

volcano

Rocks get weathered by chemical, physical and biological weathering.

Small fragments of rock get transported away from rock faces by rain, streams and rivers.

When the river slows down, the bits of rock are deposited at the bottom of the river, or sea. Over many years, these bits of rock build up to form layers.

sediment

The layers of sediment gradually get squashed and eventually form sedimentary rock.

Some magma gets trapped, and cools underground to form igneous rocks with large crystals.

Magma rises to the surface of the Earth.

Some igneous rocks are changed into metamorphic rocks.

Some sedimentary rocks get heated and squashed by earth movements under the surface of the Earth. This changes the rock into metamorphic rock.

If the rock is heated enough, it melts and forms magma.

1 How are sedimentary rocks formed?
2 How are igneous rocks formed?
3 How are metamorphic rocks formed?

A The rock cycle.

The rock cycle has been making and changing rocks since the Earth was formed. The surface of the Earth is divided into plates, which move very slowly. The earth movements that can cause rocks to be buried or volcanoes to form happen because these plates are moving.

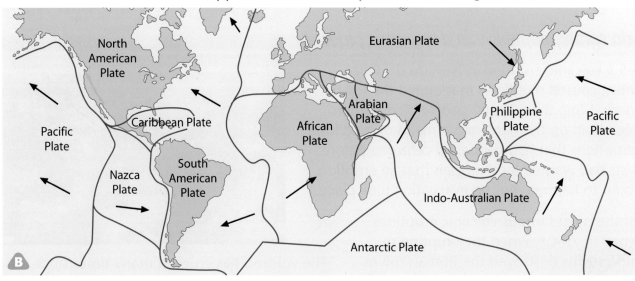

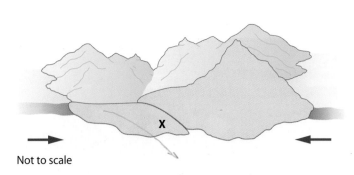

Not to scale

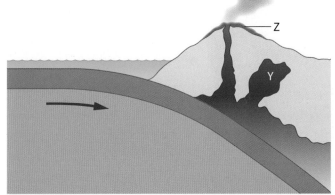

C *Where the plates push into each other, rocks are crumpled up and compressed. Mountains form, and some rocks get buried. The movement of the plates can cause earthquakes.*

D *Sometimes one plate gets pushed beneath another one. Magma from the plate can form volcanoes.*

4 What causes earthquakes?

5 Look at diagram C. What kind of rocks could be formed at point X? Explain your answer. Ⓗ Ⓢ Ⓦ

6 Look at diagram D. What size grains will the rocks have at:
  a point Y b point Z?
  c Explain your answers. Ⓗ Ⓢ Ⓦ

I CAN...

o describe how the rock cycle links together the processes of rock formation.

o use the idea of plates to describe places where different types of rock may be formed. Ⓗ Ⓢ Ⓦ

8He Living in danger

Why do some people live in dangerous places?

In 1985 a volcanic eruption in Nevado del Ruiz, Colombia, caused mudflows that buried the town of Armero. More than 23 000 people died. Armero had been built on the hardened remains of mudflows from eruptions that had happened centuries before. Scientists had warned local officials that an eruption was about to happen, but no evacuation took place.

One of the most famous volcanic eruptions happened in 79 CE, when the eruption of Mount Vesuvius destroyed the Roman towns of Pompeii and Herculaneum.

A

The volcano has erupted many times since, sometimes killing many people and destroying nearby villages. It has not erupted since 1944, but it is possible that it could erupt again with very little warning.

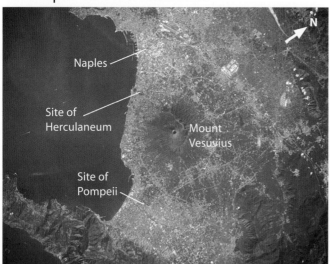

B *Almost 3 million people live around the slopes of Mount Vesuvius in Italy. There are plans to evacuate people if the volcano erupts, but it could take weeks to remove everyone from the danger zone.*

C *Archaeologists excavating Pompeii. They remove the ash from the eruption to find out about the buildings and the people who lived there.*

1 a What kind of rock is formed when volcanoes erupt?
  b Describe how two other types of rock are formed.
2 If the volcano stopped erupting, it would eventually get smaller. How would this happen?
3 a Suggest why people choose to live near hazards such as volcanoes.
  b People could be saved if everyone was evacuated at the first sign that the volcano might erupt. Suggest why this does not happen.

HAVE YOUR SAY

Should people be allowed to live in areas where they might be killed by earthquakes or eruptions?

8la Keep your cool

How Science works

Humans live in many different environments all over the world. Some places where humans live are very hot, and some are very cold.

A *Inuit people can live in very cold climates, because their clothing and homes help to keep them warm.*

B *The clothes that these Tuareg men are wearing help to keep them cool.*

The temperature of the human body is 37°C. If the inside of our body gets more than a few degrees warmer or cooler than this, we die. Our bodies have ways of keeping us at the right temperature, such as sweating and shivering. However, we cannot live in very hot or very cold places without helping our bodies to stay at the right temperature. We do this by wearing clothes, which slow down the transfer of heat energy between our bodies and our surroundings. We also use buildings to shelter from heat or cold.

1 How do you measure the temperature of something?

2 Could humans live in the UK without clothes? Explain your answer.

3 a Which materials do you think are best at keeping you warm?
  b Explain why you think these materials are best.

4 A flask can keep hot drinks hot. Explain why it can also keep cold drinks cold.

C *Firefighters wear protective clothing to help them to survive in burning buildings. The manufacturers of the clothing test it using dummies like 'Pyroman'.*

What is the difference between heat and temperature?

Heat and **temperature** are related but not the same. We can measure temperature with a thermometer but we cannot measure the amount of heat energy something contains using one.

- Temperature describes how hot or cold an object is and it is usually measured in **degrees Celsius (°C)**.
- Heat is a form of energy and, like all energy, is measured in **joules (J)**. Another name for heat energy is **thermal energy**.

The amount of heat energy stored in something depends on:

- its temperature   • its material   • its mass.

1 a What is the difference between heat energy and temperature?
  b What units are used to measure them?

2 Why don't you get burned by the sparks from a sparkler?

A *Each spark given off by the sparkler is at a very high temperature, but the sparks do not have enough heat energy to burn your hand.*

temperature of water = 60 °C

B *It takes two minutes to heat the water in the kettle to 60 °C. It takes over an hour to heat the tank full of water to 60 °C.*

3 Look at drawing B.
  a Which contains the greatest mass of water: the kettle or the water tank?
  b Is the water in the kettle or tank storing the greatest amount of energy? Explain your answer.
  c Why do you think it takes longer to heat the water in the tank to 60 °C?

C These scientists in Antarctica can only live and work here because they have special clothes and buildings.

The lowest temperature recorded on the surface of the Earth was −89.2 °C, measured at the Vostok Research station in Antarctica, in July 1983. The warmest temperature recorded here was −19 °C.

Which volume of water will heat up the quickest?

- Design an investigation to find out how long it takes to heat the water in each beaker to 60 °C.
- How will you make your investigation fair?

D

Heat energy always flows from a hot object to a cool one. The bigger the difference in temperature, the faster the heat is **transferred**. The cool object becomes hotter and the hot object becomes cooler until they are both at the same temperature.

The air is warmer than the drink. Heat is transferred from the air to the drink.

Jenna's body is warmer than the air. Heat is transferred from her body to the air.

E

4 Look at photo E. Will heat flow from the drink into Jenna's hand, or from her hand to the drink? Explain your answer. Ⓗ Ⓢ Ⓦ

5 Explain your answers to these questions. Ⓗ Ⓢ Ⓦ
  a What happens to the temperature of a drink when you put an ice cube into it?
  b What happens to the temperature of the ice cube?
  c What will happen to the temperature of the drink if you leave it standing in the kitchen for a whole day?

6 Jatin says, 'We don't know what the coldest temperature on the Earth is.' Give as many reasons as you can why he is right. Ⓗ Ⓢ Ⓦ

7 Find out where and when the hottest temperature on Earth was recorded. Ⓗ Ⓢ Ⓦ

I CAN...

- recall the units for measuring temperature and energy.
- describe the difference between temperature and heat energy. Ⓗ Ⓢ w
- list the three things that the amount of heat energy in something depends on.
- recall that heat energy flows from hotter to colder objects.

How is heat energy transferred through solids?

A **conductor** is something that lets energy flow through it. When heat energy travels through solids, this is called **conduction**. Some materials are better heat conductors (or **thermal conductors**) than others. A poor heat conductor is called a heat **insulator**. Metals are good heat conductors. Materials such as wood and plastic are good heat insulators.

> **1 a** Why are saucepans usually made from metal?
> **b** Why are saucepan handles usually made from wood or plastic?
>
> **2** Draw a table to show which of these materials are heat conductors, and which are heat insulators.
> wool   plastic   aluminium foil   wood
> paper   copper   air

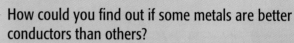

How could you find out if some metals are better conductors than others?

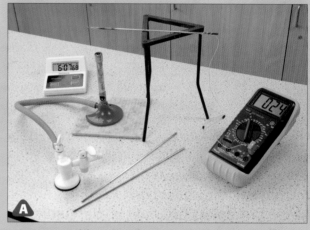

o How would you make your investigation fair?
o How could you use a temperature probe and computer to take measurements?

You can tell whether something is a conductor or an insulator by touching it. If you walk around in your bare feet, tiles feel colder than carpets. This is because tiles are better heat conductors than carpets. The heat is conducted away from you quickly by the tiles, so your feet feel cold.

Carpets are good heat insulators because they contain trapped air. Air is a good heat insulator if it cannot move. The feathers on birds trap air and help to keep the birds warm. We can use feathers in duvets to keep us warm in bed.

> **3** Why does a plastic fizzy drink bottle usually feel warmer than a metal can of drink even if they are at the same temperature?
>
> **4** Look at photo B. Why is the jacket a good insulator?

B *This jacket is filled with lots of tiny feathers. It is a very good insulator.*

The particle model of matter can help to explain why some substances let heat flow through them easily and some do not.

When a solid is heated the particles in it gain energy and vibrate more. The particles bump into each other and pass the energy on. Conduction happens best in solids because the particles are very close together. Conduction does not take place very well in liquids. It hardly happens at all in gases because the particles are a long way apart.

The particles in the metal bar gain heat energy and vibrate faster.

The vibrations are passed along the bar, so these particles will also begin to vibrate faster.

C

5 Explain how heat is conducted through a solid object. Use ideas about particles in your answer. Ⓗ Ⓢ Ⓦ

6 Why are solids better heat conductors than liquids? Ⓗ Ⓢ Ⓦ

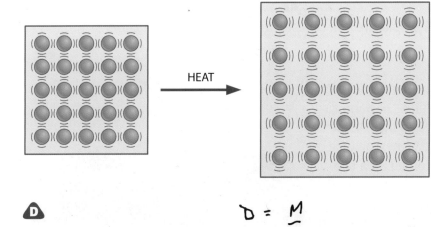

HEAT

D

$$D = \frac{M}{V}$$

The extra vibrations in a hot solid mean that the particles need more space to move around in and so the solid **expands** (gets bigger). When the solid cools down again the particles move more slowly and the solid **contracts** (gets smaller).

When a solid expands it has the same mass, but it takes up more space. Its density decreases.

7 Why are gases heat insulators? Ⓗ Ⓢ Ⓦ

8 Why do solids expand when they are heated? Use ideas about particles in your answer. Ⓗ Ⓢ Ⓦ

I CAN...

o list materials that are good heat conductors and good heat insulators.
o explain conduction in terms of the particle model of matter. Ⓗ Ⓢ w
o explain why materials expand when they are heated. Ⓗ Ⓢ w

How does heat energy travel through liquids and gases?

Liquids and gases are all **fluids**. Heat energy does not travel through fluids very well by conduction, but it can travel by **convection**.

When a fluid is heated, the particles move around faster. The fluid expands and it becomes less dense. This is because the same mass of fluid is taking up more space. If only part of the fluid is being heated, that part starts to rise because it is less dense than the cooler fluid around it. Cooler fluid moves in to take its place, and a **convection current** forms.

As the warm water gets near the top of the beaker it is pushed sideways by more warm water coming up.

The warm water has transferred some of its heat energy to the rest of the water in the beaker. It starts to sink again.

This part of the water is warmer than other parts. It becomes less dense and starts to rise.

Cooler water takes the place of the rising warmer water.

The movement of water around the beaker is called a convection current.

A *A purple dye can be used to show a convection current.*

1 a What is a fluid?
  b Write down three examples of fluids.
2 a What happens to the density of a fluid when it is heated?
  b What happens to the heated fluid if it is warmer than the fluid around it?

Ⓗ Ⓢ Ⓦ

How can you use ideas about expanding liquids to make a thermometer?
- How will you know which temperatures it is showing?
- Explain how it works.

Some birds use rising columns of warm air to keep them in the air. The highest altitude recorded for a bird was when a Ruppell's vulture hit an airliner at 11 300 m (11.3 km)!

B

Convection currents play a large part in the weather. Some parts of the Earth are warmed more than others by the Sun. Warm places on the Earth heat the air above them, and convection currents form. We feel these currents as wind.

Convection currents can also form when part of a fluid is colder than its surroundings.

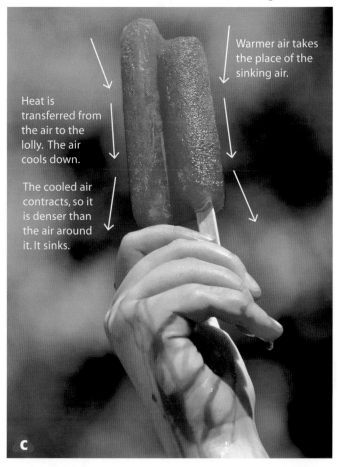

Warmer air takes the place of the sinking air.

Heat is transferred from the air to the lolly. The air cools down.

The cooled air contracts, so it is denser than the air around it. It sinks.

C

3 Why will air sink if it is colder than the air around it?

4 Copy this diagram, and add arrows to show the direction of the convection current caused by the ice cube. Ⓗ Ⓢ Ⓦ

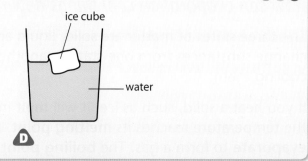

ice cube

water

D

Ⓔ *The fleece material in this jacket contains lots of air pockets. The jacket works best if it is not too baggy.*

Ⓗ Ⓢ Ⓦ

French scientist Gaspard-Gustave Coriolis (1792–1843) discovered that the rotation of the Earth causes a force that affects winds differently in each hemisphere. In the northern hemisphere hurricanes turn anticlockwise and in the southern hemisphere hurricanes turn clockwise.

5 Look at photo B on page 122.
  a Why is the jacket a good insulator?
  b Why does the air have to be trapped inside the filling of the jacket?

6 Look at the jacket in photo E. Explain why the jacket does not work so well if it is too big for the person.

7 Use ideas about particles and convection to explain how a hot air balloon flies. Ⓗ Ⓢ Ⓦ

I CAN...

o recall that liquids and gases are all fluids.
o describe the convection currents formed by hot or cold objects.
o use ideas about particles to explain how heat is transferred in fluids. Ⓗ Ⓢ W

How can evaporation cool things down?

The three states of matter are solid, liquid and gas. You can change substances from one state to another by heating or cooling them.

If you heat a solid, such as ice, it will **melt** into a liquid when the temperature reaches its **melting point**. Liquid water will **evaporate** to form a gas. The **boiling point** of a liquid is the temperature when the liquid is evaporating as fast as it can.

You can change a gas into a liquid by cooling it down until the gas **condenses** into a liquid. If you cool a liquid, it starts to turn into a solid when the temperature reaches its **freezing point**. The freezing point and melting point of a substance are always the same temperature.

If you plot a graph of temperature against time when you heat a pure substance, you get a graph like this. We can explain the shape of the graph using ideas about particles.

1 **a** What is the melting point of ice?

   b What is the freezing point of water?

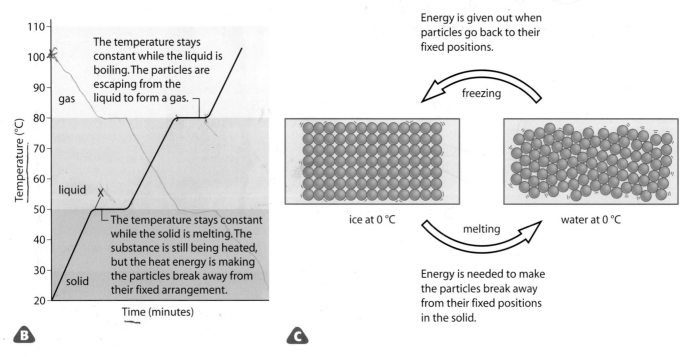

The temperature stays constant while the liquid is boiling. The particles are escaping from the liquid to form a gas.

The temperature stays constant while the solid is melting. The substance is still being heated, but the heat energy is making the particles break away from their fixed arrangement.

Energy is given out when particles go back to their fixed positions.

freezing

ice at 0 °C

melting

water at 0 °C

Energy is needed to make the particles break away from their fixed positions in the solid.

Changing from a solid to a liquid needs energy to break the bonds holding the particles together. When a liquid turns back into a solid this energy is no longer needed and is transferred to the surroundings.

2 Look at graph B. H S W
   a What is the melting point of the substance shown in the graph?
   b What is its boiling point?

3 Why does the temperature of the substance stop rising at point X?

4 Sketch a graph similar to graph A to show what happens when a substance cools down. Add labels to explain the shape of your graph. H S W

Sweating helps to cool you down. When your body is too hot, your skin produces sweat. The sweat absorbs heat from your body as it evaporates.

Dogs do not sweat. They keep cool by panting instead. When a dog breathes in, heat is transferred from its body to the cooler air in its lungs. This warmed air passes out through its mouth and water from its tongue evaporates, helping to cool it even more.

E *This shirt 'wicks' sweat. Wicking is when the sweat can spread out easily through the fabric so it can evaporate.*

H S W

Is it important to keep your body dry if you are out in cold weather?
- How can you find out if a warm body cools down faster if it is wet?
- What will you use as a model for a body?

100°C

5 Look at photo E.
   a Where does the heat come from to help the sweat to evaporate?
   b What would happen when he stops running if the sweat has not all evaporated?

6 Many outdoor jackets are 'breathable'. This means that they let water vapour (a gas) out, but do not let liquid water in. Explain why breathable fabrics can help to keep you warm.

7 If steam condenses on your hand it is more painful than dropping boiling water on your hand. Explain this as fully as you can. H S W

I CAN...

- explain what happens when a substance changes state using ideas about particles and energy. H S W

- explain some of the features of outdoor clothing. H S W

● ● ● **127**

In what other ways can heat energy be transferred?

There is nothing but empty space between the Sun and the Earth, so heat cannot travel from the Sun to the Earth by conduction or convection. All the heat we get from the Sun travels as **radiation** (sometimes called **infrared radiation**).

Infrared radiation is similar to light. It does not need anything (a **medium**) to travel through, and it can also go through transparent substances like air or glass.

All hot things give out or **emit** infrared radiation. When radiation hits something, it can be **absorbed** (taken into the object) or **reflected**. Light coloured, shiny materials reflect the most infrared radiation.

1 Why can't heat energy travel through space by conduction or convection?

2 Is the food being cooked by conduction, convection or radiation? Explain your answer.

A

B The fire is radiating heat. The campers stay warm because they are absorbing the heat.

C Infrared radiation and light can both be focused using a magnifying glass.

3 Describe three ways in which infrared radiation and light are similar.

Thermal imagers are instruments that create pictures of heat rather than light. They measure infrared radiation and convert the data into maps of temperatures. Thermal imaging can be used for filming things at night, and for finding the temperature of remote parts of the Earth by taking photographs from space.

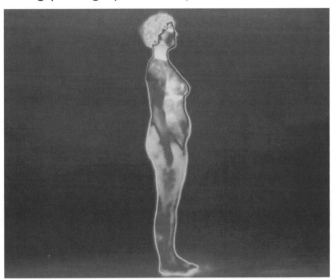

E *This thermal image shows the temperature of different parts of the human body. The hottest parts show up as white and red and cooler parts are yellow, green and blue. People who design outdoor clothing can use images like this to decide which part of their clothes need the best insulation.*

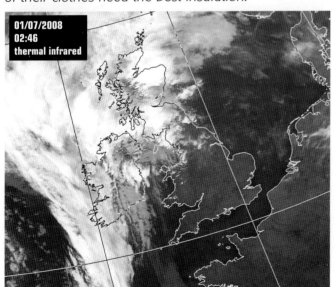

01/07/2008
02:46
thermal infrared

F *Thermal imagers on satellites can take pictures of clouds to help forecast the weather. This photo was taken at 02:46. Cold, high clouds show up as white. Low clouds, or the surface of the Earth, look dark.*

The geologist is wearing a safety suit for protection against heat radiated by the lava.

- How could you find out how the colour of the suit affects the amount of radiation it reflects?
- How could you make sure your test is safe?

D

4 What is a thermal image?

5 Look at photo E. (H)(S)(W)
  a Which parts of the body are the hottest?
  b Which parts of the body will lose heat the fastest?
  c You are designing clothes to be worn in very cold weather. Which parts would you make the thickest? Explain your answer.

6 Look at photo F. Photos of clouds can also be taken by satellites using visible light.
  a Give one advantage of using a thermal imaging camera instead of one that uses visible light.
  b Give one disadvantage.

7 Design a table to show how heat can travel through transparent and opaque solids, liquids and gases. Use the words convection, conduction and radiation at the top of three columns of the table. (H)(S)(W)

I CAN...

- recall that heat can travel by radiation.
- explain how infrared radiation is similar to light.
- describe some ways of using infrared radiation. (H)(S) W

How is protective clothing developed?

HowScienceWorks

Many different people need protective clothing. Everyone in the UK needs a waterproof coat and clothes to keep them warm or to protect them from too much sunshine. Some people need more specialist clothing.

A *This worker needs clothing to protect him from high temperatures and splashes of molten metal.*

B *These safety suits are designed to keep the passengers alive as long as possible if the helicopter has to ditch them in the sea. If they are worn with the correct insulating clothing underneath, a person should be able to survive for 3 hours in a cold sea.*

Someone who wants to develop new safety clothing needs to know what the hazards are likely to be. For example, a coat that would keep someone warm when they are walking to the supermarket does not need to be as well insulated as a coat to be worn by a scientist working in the Arctic.

Suits such as the one shown in photo B have to meet certain standards. These are set by the European Union or by the Civil Aviation Authority.

1 What are the hazards in the situations shown in:
   a photo A   **b** photo B?

2 A jacket good enough for working in the Arctic would also keep you warm going to school. Why don't manufacturers just make one kind of jacket?

3 **a** Why is it necessary for government organisations to set standards for protective clothing?
   b Write a list of requirements for a survival suit such as the ones shown in photo B. Remember that it is intended to be used by helicopter passengers. Explain your reasoning.

The effectiveness of protective clothing depends on the materials used to make it and on the design of the garment. The design features include things like:
• how well it fits
• whether it is easy to put on and take off
• whether the person can move freely when wearing it
• how hardwearing it is.

The materials that a designer is thinking of using can be tested to find out properties such as how much heat they allow through. However, the final garment also needs to be tested, to make sure that the insulation properties are not reduced by the addition of zips or by curving the fabric around a body.

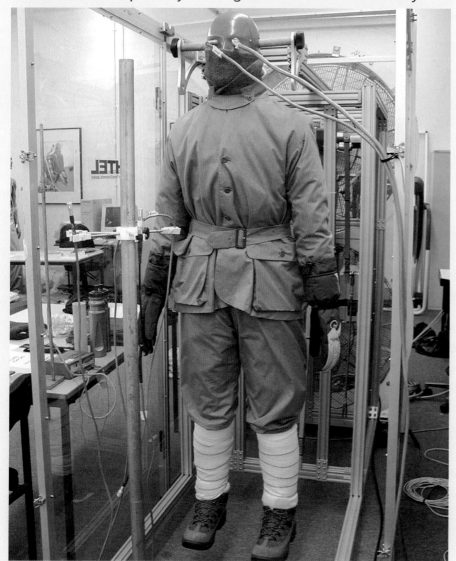

C *This manikin is used to test clothing. It has heaters inside it and sensors under different parts of its 'skin'. The mechanism behind it moves it to simulate walking. In this photo the manikin is being used for historical research. It is wearing clothing similar to that worn by the 1924 expedition to climb Mount Everest.*

!

Some protective clothing contains cooling tubes that are woven into the fabric. Liquid can circulate in these tubes, carrying heat away from the body. This technology is used in space suits and in the suits worn by Formula 1 mechanics.

4 Why is it necessary to test a finished garment, rather than just testing the fabric it is made from?

5 Look at photo C. Why are the following features of the manikin important:
  a the heaters inside it
  b the walking mechanism
  c the sensors under its surface
  d a 'sweating skin'
  e the computer?

6 The tests that are carried out on a garment depend on the purpose of the garment. List the tests that should be carried out on the clothing shown in photos A and B.

8Ie Exploring the Earth

Should we use science to help us to explore the Earth?

No-one had seen the continent of Antarctica until about 1820. The first men to reach the South Pole arrived there in 1911 and many had died on earlier expeditions. Now modern technology allows anyone with enough money to take a holiday in Antarctica. Over 30 000 people visit Antarctica every year.

A Captain Scott (1868–1912) on an expedition to the South Pole.

B

C Litter left behind by a scientific expedition.

Visiting tourists can disturb wildlife and leave seeds that are not native to Antarctica. Shellfish or other creatures that live on the outside of ships are now found in Antarctica and one accident with a ship could pollute a long length of coastline with oil.

Technological developments have allowed people to visit other parts of the Earth that used to be out of reach to humans. Today, almost anyone who is fit enough and has enough money can get to the top of Mount Everest, the highest mountain on Earth. It is a dangerous adventure; for every 50 people that reach the summit, one climber dies.

modern materials for insulated clothing

bottled oxygen to breathe in the thin air

strong and light climbing equipment

D The summit of Mount Everest.

1 a List the changes in technology that have allowed Antarctica to become a tourist destination.
b Some people think that scientific expeditions should be allowed to visit Antarctica, but not tourists. What do you think?

2 How does modern technology help people to climb high mountains? Give as many ways as you can.

3 Explain how the clothing shown in photo D works, using ideas about particles and energy.

HAVE YOUR SAY

Should we use scientific ideas to invent clothing and other technology that allows people to:
• go to dangerous places and risk their lives
• visit areas where they can easily damage the environment?

8Ja On the move

We depend on transport for almost everything we do. Our food and clothes are carried long distances by ships and lorries, and we use cars, buses and bicycles for getting around.

A *The first people to make controlled, powered aeroplane flights were the Wright brothers. Their first powered flight was on 17th December 1903, in the USA. The flight lasted 12 seconds, and only reached a height of about 3 metres! The* Wright Flyer *had a petrol engine.*

B *The first 'car' was built in 1796 in France by Nicholas Cugnot. It was powered by steam, and could move at about 2 miles per hour. This drawing shows the first car crash!*

C *A modern snowmobile, with skis and caterpillar tracks for moving fast over snow. Some snowmobiles can move at over 100 miles an hour.*

There are other uses of transport that are not as obvious. For example, electricity is generated in power stations, which all need transport to be built, and transport to find and obtain the fuels used in the power stations.

Until about 200 years ago the main forms of power for transport were wind power for ships, and animal power for land transport.

1 a Write down as many different types of transport as you can.
  b For each one, say where or how it is used, and what special features it has.
2 a Write down all the different energy resources that can be used to make vehicles move.
  b For each energy resource, list some vehicles that use it.
  c Write down some of the advantages and disadvantages of each energy resource.
3 How would your life be different if the only forms of transport were powered by the wind or by animals?

What is drag and how can it be reduced?

Any object moving through water or air will have a resistance force on it which will slow it down. **Water resistance** and **air resistance** are types of **drag**. When they design new vehicles, engineers try to reduce drag by giving the object a **streamlined** shape and making the area that faces the oncoming air or water as small as possible. The surface of the vehicle should also be as smooth as possible to reduce drag.

> **1 a** What is drag?
> **b** How can drag be reduced?

A lorry travelling at a steady speed has **balanced forces** on it. There is a force from the engine to balance the forces of drag and friction. If the drag is less, the lorry will not need such a big force from the engine, and it will not use up as much fuel. Lorries can be fitted with deflectors to reduce their drag.

A The SR-71 Blackbird holds the record for the fastest aeroplane, with a top speed of over 2000 mph. It has a streamlined shape to make the air resistance as low as possible.

H S W

How can you find out which shape has the least drag?
- What will you use to make your shapes?
- What liquid will you use for your investigation?
- What will you need to keep the same for a fair test?

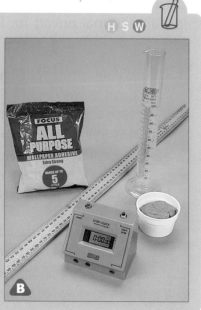

B

deflector

C

Athletes often need to make their drag as small as possible.

2 a How can the drag on lorries be reduced?
  b Why is this important? Ⓗ Ⓢ Ⓦ
3 a Describe two ways in which the cyclist in photo D has reduced his drag.
  b Explain how reducing his drag helps him to go faster.

Ⓓ *Riders on bikes like this can achieve speeds of over 130mph!*

The amount of drag on a moving object depends on its speed as well as its shape. You can feel this yourself on a windy day – the faster the wind, the more force you feel. Air resistance on a car is greater if it is moving faster, so a car uses up more fuel when it travels faster.

Drag is caused when water or air particles hit the moving object and bounce off it. Each particle produces a tiny force that slows the object down. Millions of particles hit the object each second, so the overall force can be very big. The moving particles also transfer energy to the object, which can heat up.

Speed (mph)	Miles per litre of fuel
50	9.0
60	7.9
70	6.3

Ⓔ *Fuel consumption of a car at different speeds.*

At high speeds, there are more impacts of the particles each second, and they hit the object harder, so the drag force is greater. If the *shape* of the object is streamlined, many of the particles get swept around it instead of hitting it and so the drag force is less.

Ⓕ *Smoke being used in a wind tunnel to show how the air flows over a car.*

4 Use ideas about particles to explain how a lorry deflector uses drag. Ⓗ Ⓢ Ⓦ
5 a Why do objects heat up if they are moving fast?
  b Use ideas about particles to explain why the drag is less if an object is moving slowly.
6 Write a 20 second radio advert explaining to drivers why they should drive more slowly. Ⓗ Ⓢ Ⓦ
7 a Suggest two ways in which a car designer could increase the top speed of a new car. Ⓗ Ⓢ Ⓦ
  b Explain why each way would work, using ideas about balanced forces. Ⓗ Ⓢ Ⓦ

I CAN...

○ use ideas about particles to explain what drag is and how to reduce it. Ⓗ Ⓢ W
○ use ideas about balanced forces to explain why reducing drag reduces cars' fuel consumption. Ⓗ Ⓢ W

Why do trains and bulldozers need tracks?

Pressure is the amount of *force* pushing on a certain *area*. The size of the pressure depends on the size of the force, and the size of the area it is pushing on. If there is high pressure under the wheel of a vehicle, it is more likely to sink into mud, sand or snow.

If you keep the size of the force the same:
• for a large area, the pressure will be low
• for a small area, the pressure will be high.

If you keep the area the same:
• for a large force, the pressure will be high
• for a small force, the pressure will be low.

The units for pressure are **pascals** (**Pa**). 1 Pa is a force of 1 N on an area of 1 m². Pressure can also be measured in N/cm².

A *This car has got stuck in the mud.*

1 Look at the car in photo A. Is the pressure under its wheels too high or too low?
2 Explain why the mining machine in photo B needs caterpillar tracks.
3 a Why do tractors often have very large tyres?
  b Why do many lorries have several sets of wheels?

B *This mining machine has large caterpillar tracks which spread its weight over a big area. The large area of the tracks spreads out the weight of the machine and makes the pressure under it smaller. This helps to stop the vehicle sinking into the soil. Look at the size of the people.*

A single train can transport thousands of tonnes of freight. There is a large force on the ground beneath the train. The tracks spread out the weight of the train so the wagons do not sink into the ground.

4 Explain how the pressure beneath a train is made as low as possible.

The engine and the wagons have several sets of wheels.

The train runs on steel tracks.

The tracks are laid on rows of sleepers.

The sleepers sit on a bed of ballast (stones).

C

Pressure affects everyday things as well. It is easier to cut something with a sharp knife than with a blunt one. The sharp knife has a smaller edge, so the force you put on the knife is more concentrated.

H S W !

The pressure under a vehicle matters even on a tarmac surface. These dips have been caused by cars using the car park.

D

lugs

E The wide tracks and the skis stop the snowmobile sinking into the snow. The lugs on the tracks dig into snow or ice to give grip.

5 You put the same force on a blunt knife and a sharp one. Which knife has the higher pressure under it? Explain your answer.

6 Why is it easier to push a drawing pin into the wall than to make a hole in the wall with your thumb?

7 Look at photo E. Explain how the tracks and the lugs work. Use ideas about pressure in your answer. H S W

I CAN...

- explain how pressure depends on the size of a force and the area it is pushing on.
- describe how the pressure beneath vehicles can be reduced.
- describe some everyday applications of pressure. H S W

How were railway locomotives developed?

HowScienceWorks

Engineers have been working to improve transport ever since the invention of the steam engine. The steam engine was invented by Thomas Newcomen (1663–1729), who built an 'atmospheric engine' in 1712 that was used to pump water out of mines. Many engineers worked on steam engines, trying to make them more efficient.

The first person to use a steam engine to pull wagons was Richard Trevithick (1771–1833), a Cornish inventor. His first inventions ran on roads, but in February 1804 he used a steam locomotive to pull wagon loads of iron on wooden rails from the Penydaren Ironworks to the Glamorganshire Canal. The ten mile journey took over four hours. The wooden rails were used for wagons pulled by horses, and were not all strong enough to bear the weight of the locomotive so some of them broke.

Trevithick tried to get other people interested in his steam locomotives. He built one called *Catch me who can* which went as fast as 12 mph, but it had to be dismantled after it derailed.

George Stephenson (1781–1848) was an engineer who lived in the north east of England. He became interested in steam engines when he worked at a coal mine, where engines were used for pumping water from the mine. His employer agreed to pay for Stephenson to work on a new locomotive, and he built his first one in 1814. Stephenson with his brother James and, later, his son Robert, built a series of railway locomotives, patented a design for cast iron rails, and surveyed routes for several new railways. Mine owners liked the new engines because they were cheaper than using horses to pull their materials.

The first modern passenger railway was between Manchester and Liverpool, and was opened in September 1830. George Stephenson was the chief engineer for the railway, and had to survey the route. Local landowners did not want the railway to run across their land, and protested that sparks from the engines would set thatched roofs and woods on fire. They said that the noise would stop cows giving milk, and that the engines would explode and kill people. Even Stephenson's friends thought he was mad for suggesting that the trains could run as fast as 20 mph.

A *Wooden rails were laid to make it easier for horses to pull heavy wagons.*

B *The* Catch me who can *on show in London.*

C *The Stockton to Darlington railway carried coal and was opened in 1825. Stephenson surveyed the route and his company supplied the locomotives.*

The railway owners held a competition to see who could design the best locomotive. George and his son Robert Stephenson (1803–1859) designed the *Rocket* locomotive, which used a multi-tube boiler to produce more steam than earlier engines. It could go at speeds of 36 mph, and won the competition. Even the *Rocket* was soon out of date, with Robert Stephenson and other engineers continually making new engines with better and faster designs.

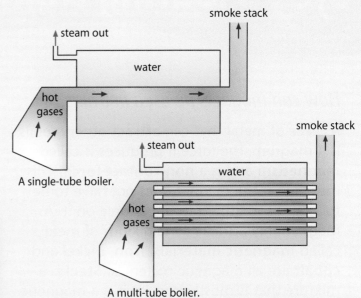

A single-tube boiler.

A multi-tube boiler.

D The Stephensons patented many of their new ideas. A patent stops other people using a new idea without the inventor's permission.

E Part of Stephenson's Rocket *in the Science Museum.*

Prizes are still offered today to encourage engineering developments. The $10 million Ansari-X prize was offered for a spaceplane, and was won by *SpaceShipOne* in 2004.

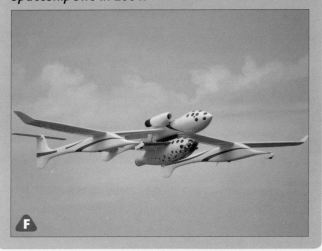

F

1 a Who built the first steam engine?
  b What was it used for?
2 Why were wooden rails laid for wagons to run on? Explain how they worked.
3 Why were mine owners interested in using steam locomotives to move their products?
4 Who built the first railway locomotive?
5 a What is a patent?
  b Why do people patent inventions?
6 Why were some people against building railways?
7 a What did the Stephensons invent that made the *Rocket* faster than other locomotives at the time?
  b Explain why this invention worked better than previous versions.

How can magnets be used in trains?

A piece of metal that can **attract** other metals is a **magnet**. The force it produces is called **magnetism** and is a **non-contact force**. This means that the magnet does not have to be touching something to put a force on it. A magnet only attracts certain kinds of metal, called **magnetic materials**. **Iron**, **nickel** and **cobalt** are all magnetic materials. **Steel** is a mixture that is mostly iron, so it is a magnetic material too. A magnet can also **repel** (push away) another magnet.

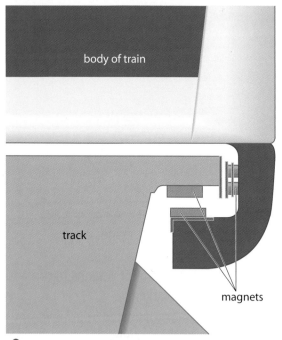

B Magnets on the maglev train are attracted to other magnets on the track.

A This is a **maglev** train. It has no wheels, and does not touch its track, so it is faster and quieter than normal trains. It is held above the track by magnets.

1 Which metals are magnetic materials?

A **bar magnet** is a magnetised piece of steel. It is a type of **permanent magnet** because it is always magnetic. The two ends of a magnet are called the **north pole** and the **south pole**.
- The north pole of a magnet will attract the south pole of another magnet.
- A north pole will repel another north pole.
- A south pole will repel another south pole.

C These magnets are repelling each other.

2 You can only prove that something is a magnet by showing that it will *repel* another magnet. Why is this? Ⓗ Ⓢ Ⓦ

How could you make a very strong electromagnet?
o Which variables would you investigate?
o How would you test the strength of your electromagnet?

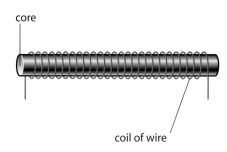

D An electromagnet.

An **electromagnet** is a magnet made using electricity. An electromagnet is only magnetic when the electric current is flowing. The direction of the north and south poles of an electromagnet depend on which way the current is flowing through the wires.

You can increase the strength of an electromagnet by:
• increasing the number of coils of wire
• increasing the current in the wire
• using a magnetic material for the core.

The magnets on the maglev train are electromagnets. A computer system controls the current very accurately to make sure that the train always stays about 15 cm above the track.

There are also electromagnets in the track that pull the train along. The computer controls the current to these magnets so that the ones just in front of the train are attracting the magnets fastened to the train. As the train moves forwards, the next set of magnets on the track are turned on by the computer, so the train is continually pulled forwards.

3 a What happens to an electromagnet if you switch the current off?
  b How is this different to a bar magnet?
4 How could you reduce the strength of an electromagnet? There are three things you could do.

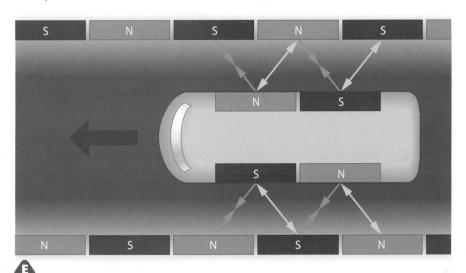

E

5 Why does controlling the current in the electromagnets help to control the maglev train?
6 Why are computers needed to run maglev trains?

The first patents for maglev trains were granted in Germany to Hermann Kemper (1892–1977) in the 1930s, but the trains could not be built then because the computer technology needed to control the electromagnets did not exist. The first commercial passenger maglev train went into service in 2004 in Shanghai, China.

I CAN...

o describe when magnets will attract and repel each other.
o investigate the variables that affect the strength of electromagnets.
o describe a real life use of electromagnets.

What are magnetic fields?

Modern ships use information from satellites and radios to work out where they are and which way to steer. Until about 50 years ago, sailors had to use a **compass** to work out the direction in which to steer.

Magnetic materials were discovered thousands of years ago. It was found that pieces of rock that contained a lot of iron would always point north if they were hung from a thread. A magnet that points north can be used as a compass.

When people made bar magnets, they named the end that pointed north the **north-seeking pole**. We call the other end of the magnet the **south-seeking pole**. These names are usually shortened to north pole and south pole.

 H S W !

Nobody knows when compasses were first used. Some people think that they were used in China over 2300 years ago, but they were certainly being used 800 years ago to help ships find their way.

1 What is a compass?
2 Why is one end of a magnet called the north-seeking pole?

The space around a magnet where it has an effect is called the **magnetic field**.

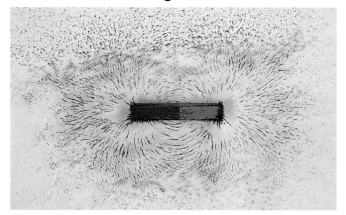

A You can see the shape of the magnetic field of a bar magnet using iron filings.

You can also find the shape of a magnetic field using a small compass.

B This compass is called a **plotting compass**. If there are no magnets near, it will point to the Earth's North Pole.

C If it is near a magnet, a plotting compass will be affected by the magnetic field of the magnet.

Scientists draw the magnetic field of a bar magnet as shown in diagram D. If you look very carefully at the photo of the iron filings, you can see that they are showing a similar shape.

The field is all around the magnet. The magnetic field is strongest where the lines are close together. The field gets weaker as you get further from the magnet. The shape of the magnetic field of an electromagnet is a similar shape. The direction of the field of an electromagnet depends on the direction the current is flowing through the coil.

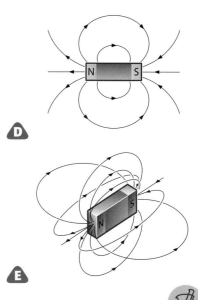

D

E

3 Describe two ways of finding the shape of a magnetic field. **H S W**
4 Draw the shape of the magnetic field around a bar magnet.

The magnetic field has a direction. This direction is the way the north pole of a compass moves near another magnet. North poles repel each other, so the direction of the magnetic field is away from the north pole of the bar magnet, and towards the south pole.

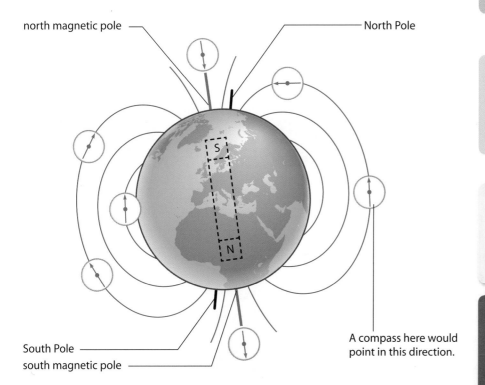

north magnetic pole — North Pole

South Pole
south magnetic pole

A compass here would point in this direction.

F *Compasses point north because the Earth has a magnetic field. Compasses point towards the north magnetic pole, which is near the North Pole. A model for helping us to understand how compasses work is to think of the Earth as having a huge bar magnet inside it.*

How could you find the shape of the magnetic field when two bar magnets are close to each other?
o What apparatus would you need?

H S W

Sir James Clark Ross (1800–1862) discovered the north magnetic pole in 1831. It has moved since he first discovered it!

5 Which way will the north pole of a compass move if it is put near the north pole of a bar magnet?

I CAN...

o describe the magnetic field of a bar magnet.
o use ideas about magnetic fields to explain how compasses work. **H S W**

How can you increase the size of a force?

All forms of transport need to be controlled, so they are safe and go where they are supposed to! Aeroplanes are controlled using special flaps on the wings and on the tail. To find out why the **ailerons** are at the ends of the wings we need to know about **levers**.

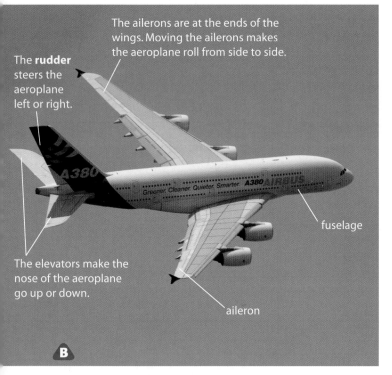

The ailerons are at the ends of the wings. Moving the ailerons makes the aeroplane roll from side to side.

The **rudder** steers the aeroplane left or right.

The elevators make the nose of the aeroplane go up or down.

aileron

fuselage

B

A These two aeroplanes are flying at different attitudes. The 'attitude' describes how much the plane is tilted compared with the horizon.

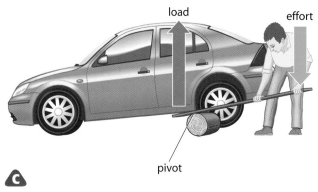

load

effort

pivot

C

Forces can move objects by turning them around a **pivot** or **fulcrum**. A long bar that pivots is a lever. When you push down on one side you are applying an **effort** and the object on the other end, the **load**, moves up. The downward force of the effort on one side causes the load on the other side to move up.

The ailerons are used to tilt the aeroplane from side to side. They are on the ends of the wings to magnify the force they provide. The wings are acting like levers.

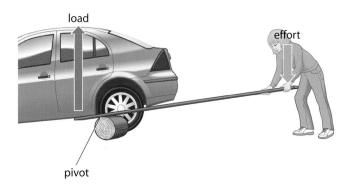

load

effort

pivot

D A longer lever makes lifting the load easier.

1 What is a lever?
2 a Why are the ailerons at the ends of an aeroplane's wings?
  b Why do you think the elevators are right at the back of the aeroplane?
3 Give another name for a pivot and explain what it is.

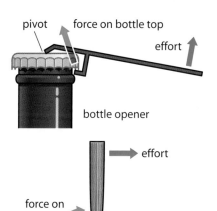

E Simple levers used at home.

We use many simple levers in the home. Most levers work by changing a small force into a larger one. The lever acts as a **force multiplier**. The smaller effort force has to move through a greater distance than the multiplied force.

Some levers can act as **distance multipliers** instead. In diagram G the elbow is acting as a pivot. The **biceps muscle** pulls on the **radius bone** and moves it a little way. The radius bone acts as a lever. The force at the hand is less than the force from the biceps muscle, but it moves further.

4 Copy the drawing, and show how you would use a spoon handle to open the tin. Label the effort, pivot and force on lid.

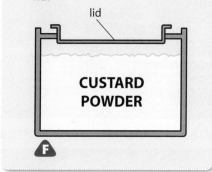

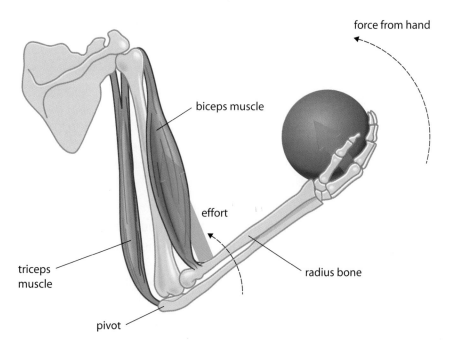

5 Explain how your hand can lift a weight using the elbow as a pivot. Use the words load and effort in your answer.
6 When you stand on tiptoes you are also using bones as levers. Where do you think the pivot is?
7 Write down some things that you can do using levers that would not be possible without them. H S W

I CAN...
o explain what a lever is.
o give some examples of uses of levers. H S W

We use transport for many things – but are all these uses of transport necessary? Almost all forms of transport need fossil fuels for energy.

HowScienceWorks

Burning fossil fuels is not **sustainable**, because we are using up non-renewable energy resources and contributing to global warming.

C *Engineers at Volkswagen are developing the '1L', which will use only 1 litre of fuel to go 100 km. It carries two passengers, sitting one behind the other, which helps to make its front area smaller and so reduce its air resistance.*

A *Do children need to be taken to school in cars?*

B *Do we need vegetables that have to be flown long distances?*

HAVE YOUR SAY

How can we make our use of transport sustainable?

1 a Write down all the forms of transport that you have used today, including transport for things like bringing the food you eat to the shops and then to your home.
  b Which of the uses of transport that you have written down are essential for your survival?
  c Which could be replaced by something more environmentally friendly (such as walking to school instead of taking the bus)?
  d Could you manage without some of the uses of transport altogether?

2 Trains can use diesel engines or electric motors to make them move.
  a What are the advantages and disadvantages of diesel engines and electric motors?
  b Which type of engine could use renewable energy resources most easily? Explain your answer.

3 a How could cars be designed to use less fuel per mile?
  b How could the government encourage car manufacturers to make more efficient cars?

8Ka What a picture!

HowScienceWorks

The first permanent photograph was taken in France in 1826 by Joseph Niépce. He had been experimenting for several years, trying to find a material that would permanently change when it was exposed to light. Eventually he found that a type of bitumen (a tar-like substance) on a metal plate would work. The bitumen hardened when it was exposed to light. The bitumen that did not harden could be washed away, leaving light and dark areas on the plate.

The latest cameras are **digital cameras**. The image is recorded and stored electronically. Digital cameras can be made small enough and cheaply enough to go inside mobile phones. They can also be put into satellites and space probes, to allow us to see **images** of things we could never see for ourselves. The engineers who design cameras need to know about light and how it behaves.

A This view from a window was the world's first photograph. It was recorded on a pewter plate over several hours.

B Some **cameras** today use a strip of plastic film coated in chemicals which change when they are exposed to light. The film has to be 'developed' to make the changes permanent.

C A digital photo of Saturn's rings, taken by the Cassini space probe.

1 Write down as many sources of light as you can.
2 Explain what these words mean:
   a transparent **b** opaque **c** shadow.
3 **a** Describe three photographs you have seen today.
   b Explain what the photos were for (for example, advertising, entertainment, education).
4 Write down two things that you have seen in photographs that you would not be able to see for yourself.

●●●**147**

How have ideas about light changed?

How**S**cience**W**orks

Empedocles (490–430 BCE) was a philosopher in ancient Greece. He suggested that **rays** shine out from our eyes and allow us to see things. Not all Greek philosophers agreed with this idea.

The Arab scientist Ibn al-Haytham (965–1038) carried out lots of experiments on light. He wrote the *Book of Optics* in which he stated that we see things when rays of light from objects go into our eyes. Scientists today agree with this idea.

There is light all around us and we cannot see anything without it. Objects that create light are **sources** of light or **luminous sources**. We see them because light spreads out in all directions from a luminous source, and some of it goes into our eyes. We can see **non-luminous** objects because light bounces off them and enters our eyes.

A *Ibn al-Haytham.*

1 Look around the room you are in at the moment.
   a Name two luminous sources.
   b Name two non-luminous things that light is bouncing off.
2 Look at photo B.
   a Which luminous sources is the man looking at?
   b How can the man see the table?

B *We can show how light travels by drawing rays. The rays have arrows to show which direction the light is travelling.*

The speed of light

As soon as you switch on a lamp you can see the light. The light actually takes time to travel from the lamp to your eyes but it is too fast for you to notice. Hundreds of years ago many scientists thought that light did not travel. It was either on or off. They thought this because they could see the lightning in a thunderstorm straight away but the sound of the thunder took longer to reach them.

C *For every three seconds between the flash of lightning and the sound of thunder, the storm is about one kilometre away.*

The Italian scientist Galileo (1564–1642) disagreed and said that thunderstorms did not prove that light was only on or off, only that light travels faster than sound. He tried to measure the speed of light by shining lanterns a mile apart. However, light travels so fast he could not work out a speed.

Olaus Roemer (1644–1710), a Dutch scientist, was the first to measure the speed of light in 1675. He worked out the speed of light by observing the moons of Jupiter at different times in Jupiter's orbit.

> 4 Roemer observed the moons of Jupiter. Which luminous source in the Solar System did the light bouncing off Jupiter's moons come from?
> 5 How long does it take for light to travel from the Sun to the Moon and then to the Earth? Give your answer in seconds.

Light takes the quickest path between any two points, so it travels in straight lines. **Shadows** are made because light cannot travel through some objects. The light cannot bend around them either.

E We can see the beams of light because dust particles in the air are scattering some of the light.

> 3 a Which travels faster, light or sound?
> b What evidence do you have that this is true?

D Our Moon. Light travels at 300 000 km/s. It takes 8.5 minutes for light from the Sun to reach the Moon, and another 1.3 seconds for light bouncing off the Moon to reach the Earth.

> 6 Describe how you could show that light travels in straight lines.

I CAN...

- explain how we can see luminous and non-luminous objects.
- explain why shadows occur.
- recall how some people tried to measure the speed of light.

How do cameras and eyes work?

When light hits an object, different things can happen to it depending on what the object is made out of. Light can travel through **transparent** materials like glass (we say that it is **transmitted**). Sometimes you can only see a glow of light through something. We say that materials like this are **translucent**. Paper is translucent. Things that light cannot travel through are called **opaque**. Opaque objects cause darker shadows than translucent ones.

Light bounces off other objects. We say that the light is **reflected** and this is how we see non-luminous objects. Light is also 'taken in' or **absorbed** by some objects. Darker objects absorb more light than paler ones. Many objects both absorb and reflect light. Light is a way of transferring energy. When an object absorbs light, the energy is transferred to heat energy and the object warms up a little.

Prism with reflective coating so that light reflects inside it.

Light is reflected by the mirror and the prism. The photographer can see exactly what will be in the photograph by looking through the **viewfinder**.

viewfinder

mirror

film or sensors

When the photograph is taken the mirror flips up out of the way. Light is absorbed by the film or by **sensors**, which record the image.

Light is transmitted through the lenses.

A *A single lens reflex (SLR) camera.*

1 Name two materials that are:
   a opaque   b transparent   c translucent.
2 Explain your answers to these questions.
   a Which will absorb more light: a dark brown coat or a pale blue coat?
   b Which will transmit more light: a piece of clear glass or a piece of paper?
   c Which reflects more light: the white background of this page or the black letters?

Scientists are working on a 'bionic eye' that will help blind people to see. A tiny video camera in a pair of spectacles sends a signal to a computer chip implanted in the retina. The chip sends tiny electrical signals into the retina, which the brain interprets as points of light.

H S W

How would you use a lamp to classify materials as transparent, translucent or opaque?
○ How could you use a datalogger to compare the amount of light reflected or transmitted?

The simplest kind of camera is a **pinhole camera**. Light goes through a tiny hole and forms an upside-down image on a screen at the back of the camera. It is called a pinhole camera because the hole can be made with a pin.

The hole in the front of a camera can be made bigger or smaller to control how much light gets in. Your eyes work in a similar way. Too much light can damage your eyes, so your pupils get smaller when it is very bright. In dim light your pupils get bigger to let in more light.

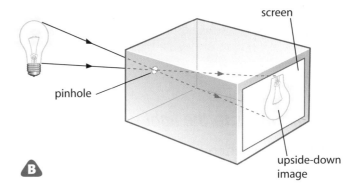

screen

pinhole

upside-down image

B

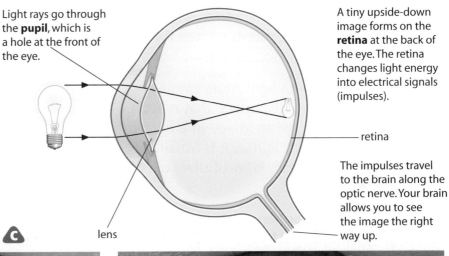

Light rays go through the **pupil**, which is a hole at the front of the eye.

A tiny upside-down image forms on the **retina** at the back of the eye. The retina changes light energy into electrical signals (impulses).

retina

The impulses travel to the brain along the optic nerve. Your brain allows you to see the image the right way up.

C

lens

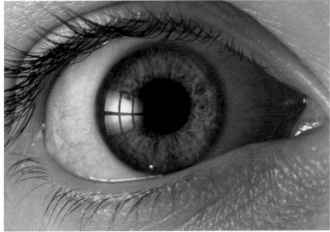

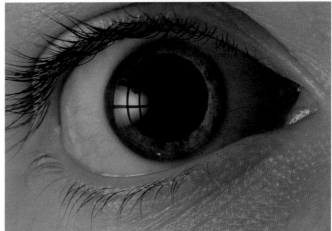

D *Pupils in bright and dim light.*

3 **a** What energy change happens in your eyes?
  b Where does this energy change happen?

4 What is a pinhole camera? How does it work?

5 Name two ways in which the eye and a camera are similar.

6 Why do the pupils in your eyes change size?

7 The chemicals on photographic film change when they absorb light. How could you modify a pinhole camera so that it took photographs?

(H)(S)(W)

I CAN...

o describe what can happen to light when it hits an object.

o explain how pinhole cameras work.

o compare the ways in which cameras and eyes work.

(H)(S)w

What happens to the light when it hits a mirror?

We see things when light reflects off them and enters our eyes. Most things reflect light in all directions, **scattering** the light unevenly. Often even things that *feel* smooth, such as a piece of paper, have a rough surface if you look at them closely.

Smoother things reflect light more evenly. A mirror has a very smooth surface that reflects light evenly. We can see an image in a mirror. A **plane mirror** is a flat mirror. It is usually made of glass with a thin layer of silver or aluminium on the back.

Professional photographers usually use single lens reflex (SLR) cameras. An SLR camera has a plane mirror inside it, and a five-sided glass prism. The mirror and the prism reflect the light transmitted through the lens to the viewfinder, so the photographer can see what the photograph will be like. The mirror flips up out of the way when the photograph is taken, so light can travel to the film or sensors.

- The ray of light which goes to the mirror is the **incident ray**.
- The ray of light which comes from the mirror is the **reflected ray**.
- The **normal** is a line which is drawn as a dashed line at right angles to the mirror. It helps us to measure the angles.
- The **angle of incidence** is the angle between the incident ray and the normal.
- The **angle of reflection** is the angle between the reflected ray and the normal.

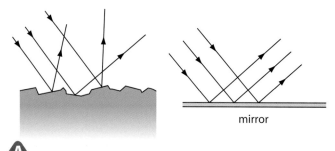

A

1 Why can't you see an image on a piece of paper?
2 a What is a flat mirror called?
  b What is it made from?

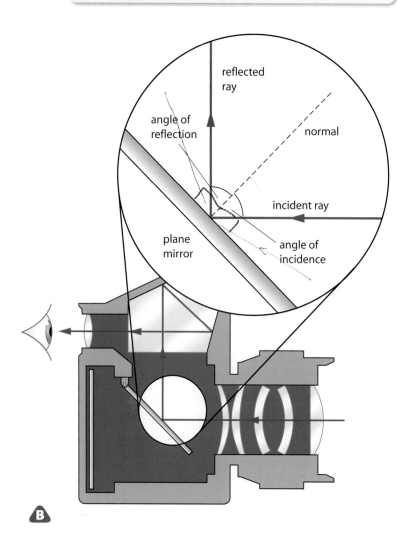

B

This **ray diagram** shows how we see an image in a mirror. Rays of light spread out in all directions from a luminous source. However, when we draw ray diagrams we only draw two rays, to keep the diagram simple.

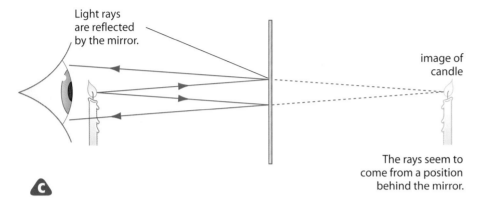

Light rays are reflected by the mirror.

image of candle

The rays seem to come from a position behind the mirror.

C

Some rules for reflections in a plane mirror

- The image is the same size as the object.
- The image is the same distance behind the mirror as the object is in front of it.
- In the image, left is right and right becomes left.
- The angle of incidence is equal to the angle of reflection. This means that the ray leaves the mirror at the same angle as it arrived at the mirror.

3 If you raise your right hand and look in a mirror, on which side of the mirror does your arm rise?

4 If you stand 4 m from a mirror, how far are you from where the image appears to be?

5

E

You can use a periscope to see over things, or to take photos over things. Draw a ray diagram to help you to explain how you would use two mirrors to make a periscope. Ⓗ⑤Ⓦ

ⒽⓢⓌ
How would you find out whether there is a relationship between the angle of incidence and the angle of reflection?

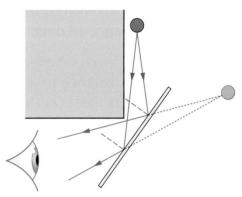

D *You can use a mirror to look at something round a corner.*

The world's biggest mirrors are curved mirrors 8.4 m in diameter. They are used in a telescope in the USA that is powerful enough to make images of planets orbiting other stars.

I CAN...

- describe how different surfaces reflect light.
- draw ray diagrams for mirrors. Ⓗ⑤w
- use ideas about angles of incidence and reflection to explain how we see images in a plane mirror. Ⓗ⑤w

How do lenses work?

Cameras and eyes both have **lenses** to make sure that the image is sharp and clear. Lenses bend light as light passes through them. This change of direction of light is called **refraction**.

Refraction happens whenever light travels from one transparent substance to another. It only takes place where two substances meet (at their **interface**). If the light passes through the interface at 90° it does not change direction.

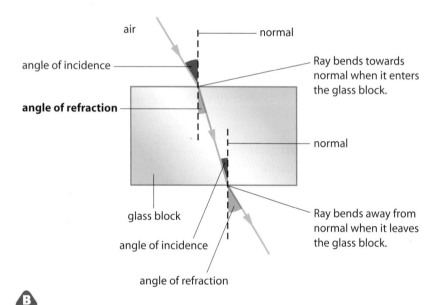

B

A This bowl of water is acting like a lens. It makes the cat's face look bigger.

1 What is refraction?
2 Why do cameras need lenses?
3 Draw a ray diagram to explain what the following are:
   a the normal
   b the angle of incidence
   c the angle of refraction.

When light travels from air to a material such as glass or water it changes direction towards the normal. When it travels out into the air it changes direction away from the normal. This happens because light travels more slowly in substances such as water or glass than it does in air.

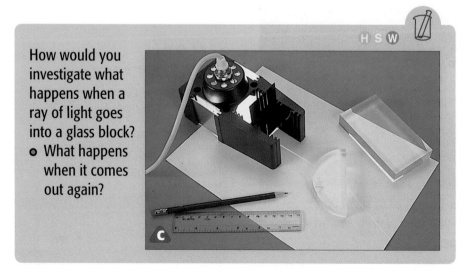

How would you investigate what happens when a ray of light goes into a glass block?
○ What happens when it comes out again?

H S W

C

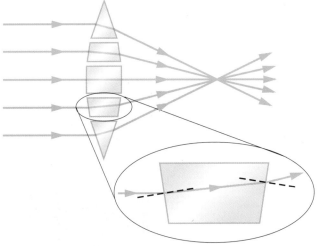

Light bends towards the normal as it goes into the lens.

It bends away from the normal as it leaves the lens.

D *It is easier to understand how a lens works if you think of it as made up of lots of separate bits of glass.*

(H)(S)(W)

How can you investigate how different lenses bend light?

4 The lens in diagram D is called a **converging lens**.
  a Describe the shape of the lens.
  b Describe what the lens does to the light rays that travel through it.
5 Converging lenses can be fat or thin. (H)(S)(W)

E

What would happen to rays of light if they shine through a lens fatter than the one in D? Draw a diagram similar to D to work out the answer.

6 Diagram G shows a diverging lens. Draw a diagram similar to diagram D to work out what this lens will do to light that shines through it.

(H)(S)(W)

G

(H)(S)(W)

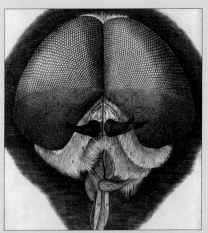

F *Lenses can be used to make small things look bigger. This drawing shows the eyes of a fly. It was drawn by Robert Hooke (1635–1703) and published in his book called* Micrographia *in 1665. Hooke did not invent the microscope, but he made improvements to existing designs.*

I CAN...

- recall how light changes direction at the interface of two different substances.
- use a model to explain how lenses work. (H)(S) W

How do we get coloured light?

We think of daylight as **white light**. But white light is made up of different colours. You can split up white light with a **prism**.

When white light passes through a prism the different colours are refracted (change direction) by different amounts, so the colours spread out. The colours of the rainbow are called a **spectrum**. Red is refracted least and violet the most. This separating of the colours is called **dispersion**. The colours in the spectrum are red, orange, yellow, green, blue, indigo, and violet.

H S W

How would you make a spectrum using a prism?
o How could you get the different coloured rays to mix together again?

1 List the colours in the spectrum.
2 How is a rainbow formed?

B Lenses also split up the colours in white light. Photographs taken with cheap cameras often show coloured fringes around objects. Good quality cameras use combinations of lenses to avoid this effect.

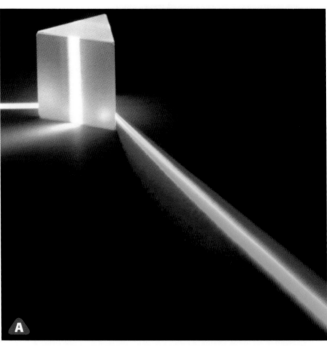

A

The rainbow was first explained by a monk called Theodoric (c.1250–c.1310), living in Germany in the fourteenth century. He said that a rainbow was caused by the Sun's rays being refracted by rain or mist.

C A rainbow is produced when water droplets in the air refract sunlight.

Isaac Newton (1642–1727) carried out experiments with prisms and coloured filters. Many people thought that the prism had added the colours to the light. Newton showed that the colours could be made back into white light with a second prism, so the first prism had only split them up.

3 How did Newton show that prisms do not add colours to light? Ⓗ Ⓢ Ⓦ

Making coloured light

Coloured light can be made from white light using **filters**. As white light passes through a filter some of the colours are absorbed. A red filter only allows red light to be transmitted through the filter and all the other colours are absorbed.

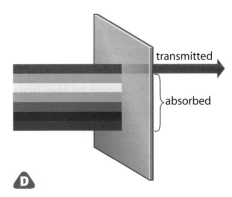

4 Explain how you can use a filter to make blue light.

Many objects look coloured because they do not reflect all the colours in light. White objects reflect *all* the colours. A red object only reflects red light and all the other colours are absorbed. This idea applies to all colours except black. Black objects absorb *all* colours.

If a coloured light shines onto an object then the object's colour may appear to change. This is because there are fewer colours to be reflected.

In white light player X's red top reflects only red light. Player Y's top reflects only blue. Player Y's shorts reflect all colours so they look white. Player X's shorts absorb all colours so they look black.

Only red light is hitting the white shorts so they can only reflect red. The blue top and black shorts absorb red so they look black.

5 a Why does a blue object look blue in white light?
   b Why do black objects appear black in white light?
6 Look at drawing E. The players stand in a blue spotlight.
   a What colour will their clothes appear to be?
   b Explain your answers.
7 Sam is wearing a white shirt, a red jacket and green trousers to a nightclub. What will his clothes look like:
   a in a red spotlight   **b** in a green spotlight
   c in a blue spotlight?   **d** Explain your answers.

I CAN...

- describe how to make a spectrum.
- explain how filters work. Ⓗ Ⓢ W
- explain the colours of objects in different lights. Ⓗ Ⓢ W

How do we see different colours?

Our eyes have a layer of cells at the back called the retina. The cells in the retina convert light energy into electrical signals. There are two main types of sensor in the retina.

- Cells called **rods** can detect low levels of light, but cannot detect the colour of the light.
- Cells called **cones** can detect colours, but cannot detect very dim light. There are three types of cones: one type detects red light, one type detects blue and one type detects green. These three colours are called the **primary colours** of light.

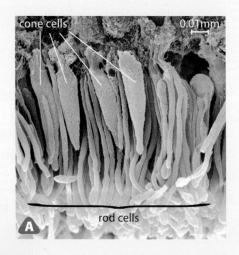

A

Our brains interpret the signals from our eyes. Diagram B shows how we 'see' different combinations of signals from the cones. Yellow, **cyan** and **magenta** are called **secondary colours**. All colours can be made from different combinations of the three primary colours.

1 Suggest why we cannot see colours very well at night.
2 What colours do we see when our eyes detect:
  a red and green light   b green and blue light?

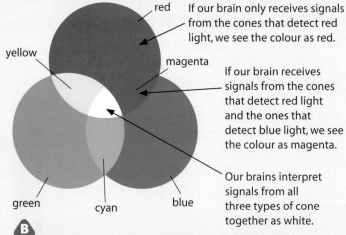

red — If our brain only receives signals from the cones that detect red light, we see the colour as red.

magenta — If our brain receives signals from the cones that detect red light and the ones that detect blue light, we see the colour as magenta.

Our brains interpret signals from all three types of cone together as white.

yellow

green   cyan   blue

B

The fact that we only need three different colours of light is very useful in showing and recording images. A television screen only needs to produce the primary colours of light, but the colour we 'see' depends on the relative brightness of the three colours at each point on the screen. Similarly, the sensors in a digital camera only need to record red, green and blue light. When we look at a photograph from a digital camera, the colours we see depend on the amount of each different colour in each part of the image.

C *A television picture is made using the three primary colours. The colour we 'see' depends on the relative brightness of the three colours at each point on the screen.*

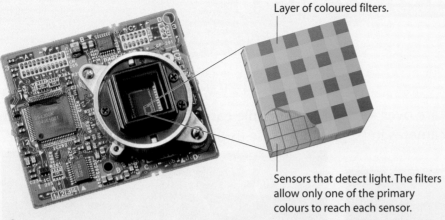

Layer of coloured filters.

Sensors that detect light. The filters allow only one of the primary colours to reach each sensor.

D *This is the part of a digital camera that detects light entering the camera.*

There are 'colours' of light that we cannot see. The light beyond violet in the spectrum is called **ultraviolet** light. Photographs can be taken using film or sensors that can detect ultraviolet light. These photos can be printed as 'false-colour' images, with the ultraviolet colours converted to colours that we can see.

The 'colour' that we cannot see beyond red light is called **infrared** radiation. We can feel this as heat, but our skin cannot make heat images! Infrared radiation from the Sun is reflected and refracted just like visible light. Different surfaces reflect different amounts of infrared, and this can be detected by special cameras.

F *A false-colour infrared image of part of Brazil. This image was taken by a satellite. Rainforest shows up as orangey red, and the dark blue areas on the left are marsh. The pale blue rectangles and lines show places where the rainforest has been chopped down.*

3 a Why do the digital sensors in a camera only need to detect three different colours?

b Which sensors will detect light when white light shines into the camera?

E

This image of a dandelion was taken using visible light.

This false-colour image was taken using ultraviolet light. Bees and other insects would be able to see this pattern, and it helps them to find the nectar in the flower.

4 Why is photo F a 'false-colour' image?

5 Suggest how satellite pictures like photo F can be useful for monitoring crops or illegal logging. **H S W**

How are cameras useful?

Cameras are all around us. There are over 4 million closed-circuit TV (CCTV) cameras in public places in the UK.

A CCTV images. Cameras in public places can be used to solve crimes – but some people think they are an invasion of privacy.

B A radar measures the speed of cars, and the camera takes a photograph of any car that is speeding.

1 Give as many examples of these uses of photography as you can:
   a preventing or solving crimes
   b scientific discoveries
   c entertainment
   d keeping people informed.
2 'The camera never lies' is an old saying.
   a What do you think this means?
   b Do you think it is correct?

How Science Works

Many people carry a camera around with them all the time as part of their mobile phone.

C Photographs of famous people help to sell newspapers and magazines.

D Digital photos can be altered using a computer.

HAVE YOUR SAY

Are cameras and photography good for society?

HowScienceWorks

Animals use sounds to communicate, to warn others of danger, to try to stop others entering their territory, to win a mate and to hunt. Some animals even use sound to see!

In 1793, Lazzaro Spallanzani (1729–1799) noticed that bats could avoid obstacles when flying in total darkness. Spallanzani blinded some bats and noticed that they could still fly around obstacles. However, he found that bats wearing hoods that covered their ears could not fly properly. Spallanzani wrote a letter to the Geneva Natural History Society suggesting that bats used their ears and not their eyes to 'see'.

This letter caught the attention of a Swiss scientist called Charles Jurine (1751–1819). In 1794, Jurine used a painless way of blocking the bats' ears to show that they did indeed use their ears to navigate. He wrote to Spallanzani, who repeated Jurine's work but could not explain it. For over a century, their work was ignored and even laughed at by scientists.

The mystery was solved in 1938 by biologist Donald Griffin (1915–2003) and physics professor G.W. Pierce (1872–1956). They worked together and used modern technology to show that bats use sounds to find their way around but these sounds are too high for humans to hear.

A This male southern elephant seal is roaring to ensure other males do not try to approach his female seals.

B You can listen to bats using a bat detector.

Recently it has been discovered, by scientists like Caitlin O'Connell, that large land mammals (e.g. giraffes, elephants) communicate using sounds too low for humans to hear.

C Caitlin O'Connell recording elephants in the Namibia.

1 How did Spallanzani and Jurine show that bats use their ears to 'see'?

2 a What was Jurine's conclusion?
  b What do you think Jurine would have observed to draw this conclusion?

3 Was Spallanzani right to blind the bats?

4 What might giraffes communicate about?

8La Sound advice

How does sound travel?

Some sounds are loud and some are soft. This is the **intensity** of the sound. Sounds with a high intensity are often said to have a high **volume**.

Sounds can also be high or low. This is the **pitch** of the sound.

B Lions and elephants can both make low pitched, high intensity sounds. A lion's roar can be heard over 5 km away.

A This skylark sings using a series of high-pitched notes.

Sounds are made by something moving backwards and forwards. This is called **vibrating**. When you speak, vocal cords in your throat vibrate. When you play a guitar the strings vibrate. Vibrating objects produce **sound waves**.

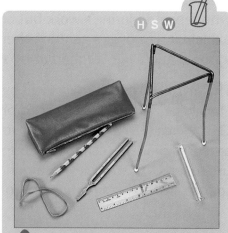

C How would you make different sounds using these items?

- What sound would you expect from each item?
- Would each item make more than one different sound?
- How would you describe the sounds?

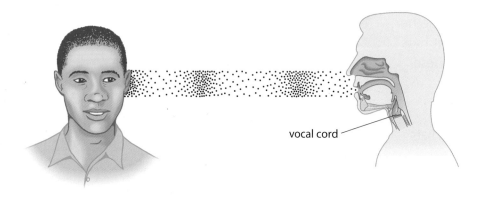

vocal cord

D When this man talks, his vocal cords vibrate to produce sound waves. The sound waves travel through the air.

1 List four animals that make loud sounds.
2 What are vibrations?
3 a List three things that vibrate to make a sound.
  b For each example, describe the pitch and the intensity of the sound.

A tuning fork is used to help musicians find a note. The fork is tapped lightly on something and the two prongs then vibrate to make a note. As the vibrating prong of a tuning fork moves in one direction, it pushes air particles. When it moves back in the other direction, it doesn't push them. When the prong swings back in the first direction, it pushes the air particles again. This causes the production of sound waves, which move away from the tuning fork.

E *This tuning fork makes 440 complete vibrations, or cycles, each second. Musicians use this to check that their instruments are correctly tuned.*

A tuning fork that produces the note A makes 440 complete backwards and forwards movements in one second. We say that the prongs complete 440 **cycles per second**.

4 How does sound travel from your mouth to someone's ear?
5 Put these tuning forks in order of the speed of vibration, starting with the slowest:
  440 cycles per second   435 cycles per second   520 cycles per second.
6 a Which of the bells in the picture below will have the highest pitch?
  b Why do you think this?
  c Which one will vibrate the fastest when hit?
  d Why do you think this is?

The tuning fork was invented in 1711 by John Shore (c.1662–1752). It helped different orchestras to tune to exactly the same note.

F

7 On a piano keyboard, the A string above middle C vibrates at 440 cycles per second.
  a Describe what 'cycles per second' means.
  b The next A string up vibrates at twice this. How many cycles per second does it vibrate at?
8 Kim says that 'cycles per second' is a measure of how fast the sound travels to the ear. Is this true? Explain your reasoning.

I CAN...

○ explain how sound waves are produced.
○ describe how sound waves travel.
○ use the terms 'intensity' and 'pitch' to describe sounds.

What are sound waves?

Scientists use **microphones** to detect animal sounds. If a microphone is attached to an **oscilloscope**, you can see a representation of the sound wave that the animal produces. By looking at the **wave** (or **trace**) on the oscilloscope screen, scientists can work out the intensity and pitch of the sound.

> **1 a** Which piece of apparatus is used to detect dolphin sounds? Ⓗ Ⓢ Ⓦ
> **b** How can scientists analyse sounds from a dolphin? Ⓗ Ⓢ Ⓦ

A Dr Denise Herzing, from The Wild Dolphin Project, analyses dolphin sound waves using software, which shows the waves in a similar way to an oscilloscope.

The sound waves from musical instruments can also be represented using an oscilloscope.

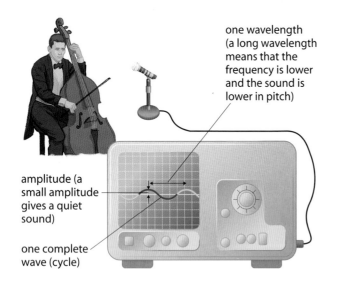

one wavelength (a long wavelength means that the frequency is lower and the sound is lower in pitch)

amplitude (a small amplitude gives a quiet sound)

one complete wave (cycle)

B This double bass is making a soft, low-pitched sound.

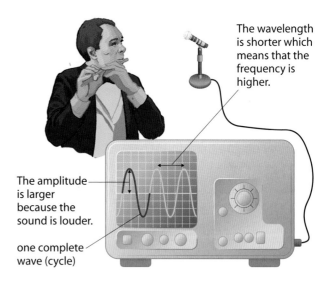

The wavelength is shorter which means that the frequency is higher.

The amplitude is larger because the sound is louder.

one complete wave (cycle)

C This piccolo is making a loud, high-pitched note.

The height of a wave is called its **amplitude**. A wave with a large amplitude makes a loud sound. Soft sounds are made by waves with small amplitudes.

The number of complete waves (cycles) passing a point each second is called the **frequency**. Frequency is measured in **hertz (Hz)**.

A wave in which 1 cycle passes a point every second has a frequency of 1 cycle per second or 1 Hz. The human ear can hear frequencies that range from 20 Hz to 20 000 Hz.

The distance between the same point on two cycles is called the **wavelength**. Waves with higher frequencies have shorter wavelengths.

2 Predict what the waves from the following will look like:
  a a loud, high-pitched violin note
  b a quiet, low-pitched saxophone note.

3 During a concert, a vocalist sings a note at the same pitch for 10 seconds, but makes it increasingly louder. Predict what the wave would look like on an oscilloscope. **H S W**

The first practical microphone was invented by the American inventor Thomas Edison (1847–1931) in 1876. This microphone was used in all telephones until the 1980s!

The French composer Olivier Messiaen (1908–1992) used to go out and write down lots of birdsong, which he used in his music. He had 'perfect pitch' – the ability to immediately identify the pitch of a note by simply listening to it.

4 What does the term 'perfect pitch' mean?

5 Why do scientists not need to have perfect pitch in order to analyse sounds? **H S W**

6 How would a scientist record birdsong? **H S W**

Many classical composers have used animal sounds to influence their work. The French composer Camille Saint-Saens (1835–1921) used different instruments to represent the sounds made by a number of different animals when he was composing *Carnival of the Animals*.

Animal	Loudness and pitch
lion	loud/low
skylark	medium/high
hyaena	loud/high
elephant	loud/low
giraffe	low/low

Instrument	Loudness and pitch
piccolo	medium/high
tuba	loud/low
double bass	loud/low
clarinet	varied/varied
violin	varied/high

E *A modern composer might use a table like this to decide which instruments can be used to represent each animal.*

7 What instrument would you choose to represent the following animals? For each one, explain your choice.
  a a lion   b a bird   c an elephant   d a hyaena.

I CAN...
- identify the different parts of a sound wave.
- describe the relationships between wave amplitude and intensity, and wave frequency and pitch.
- describe how scientists detect and analyse sounds. **H S w**

What are the similarities and differences between sound and light?

When energy is passed from one thing to another, we say that it has been **transferred**. Sound waves and light waves can both transfer energy. Sound waves transfer energy to our ears and light waves transfer energy to our eyes.

Sound waves only travel through a **medium** (any substance). They travel fastest in materials where the particles are close together and so are more likely to bump into each other and pass the vibrations on. So sounds travel faster in solids than in liquids, and they travel faster in liquids than in gases. Sound waves cannot travel through a **vacuum** (empty space).

Light is also transferred as a wave, but light can travel through a vacuum. If an explosion occurred in space, you would be able to see it, but you would not be able to hear it.

H S W

How would you find out which substances sound travels through best? Would sound travel best through:

o the bench o the water o the air?

Statement	Light	Sound
Speed in a vacuum	299 800 000 m/s	0 m/s
Speed in air (at 20 °C)	299 700 000 m/s	343 m/s
Speed in water	225 000 000 m/s	1500 m/s
Speed in steel	0 m/s	5100 m/s
Speed in glass	200 000 000 m/s	2000–6000 m/s
Can it transfer energy	Yes	Yes

A

1 Which of the following statements are true for light, true for sound or true for both light and sound:
   a fastest in air
   b travels through empty space
   c travels through a solid
   d transfers energy.

2 When sound travels from water into air, it slows down. Is this also true for light?

3 The underwater explorer Jacques Cousteau once described the sea as the silent world. Do you think this is true? Give a reason for your answer.

4 Why would you be able to hear this train before it came around the bend?

B

5 What would the time difference be between hearing sound waves through air and through the steel railway tracks if you were 3000 m from the train?

Communicating with sound and light

We communicate using both sound and light. If you want to communicate with someone next to you, you usually use sound! However, light is better to communicate with over long distances because it is better at travelling without spreading out too much and so becoming too faint. It is also quiet, so others can't hear you.

D *During the Spanish Armada, bonfires were lit to communicate to people when the ships were approaching. This photo was taken in 1988 to celebrate the 400th anniversary of the Armada.*

E *Boats near each other can communicate by using flashes of light.*

F *Information can be sent down an optical fibre in the form of light waves.*

6 List as many possible ways in which sound and light can be used to communicate as you can.

7 For the examples below, explain whether light or sound would be best for communicating:
  a with a friend who is sitting next to you
  b with a person on the other side of the world.

Male fireflies communicate to females by sending out a series of light flashes. If the female likes the flashes of light given out by the male then she might mate with him. However, some females will trick a male into mating and then eat him!

C

G *People used speaking tubes to communicate in old houses.*

I CAN...

o recall examples of how sound and light can be used to communicate.

o use and analyse data about light and sound. **H S W**

o compare sound and light waves and how they travel.

How do we hear sounds?

Most animals use ears to hear things. Many animals have a much wider range of hearing than we do. Whales can communicate using both sounds that are too low for humans to hear and sounds that are too high for us to hear.

Animal	Range
human	64–23000
dog	67–45000
cat	45–64000
rabbit	360–42000
mouse	1000–91000
gerbil	100–60000
guinea pig	54–50000
hedgehog	250–45000
bat	2000–110000
beluga whale	1000–123000
elephant	16–12000
dolphin	75–150000

0   500 1000   25000   50000   75000   100000   125000   150000

Frequency in Hz

A

> A dog's hearing is twice as sensitive as ours. For dogs, exploding fireworks sound as loud as being next to a road drill.

> How would you find out whether everyone can hear the same frequencies of sound waves?
>
> **B**
>
> A signal generator and loudspeaker will produce sound waves of set frequencies that you can listen to.

1 a Name four animals that have hearing that is different from ours.
   b Explain how their hearing is different.
2 Why can dogs hear a dog whistle but humans cannot?
3 A 'bat box' detects sounds made by bats and converts them into sounds that humans can hear. Why do scientists use bat boxes?

Sound waves travel through the air and into the ear, making the **eardrum** vibrate. These vibrations then cause the three small bones in the ear to vibrate and these in turn cause the liquid inside the **cochlea** (pronounced '**cok-lee-a**') to vibrate. The cochlea changes the sound waves into electrical signals called **impulses** that travel down a nerve to the brain. When the impulses reach the brain, we hear the sound.

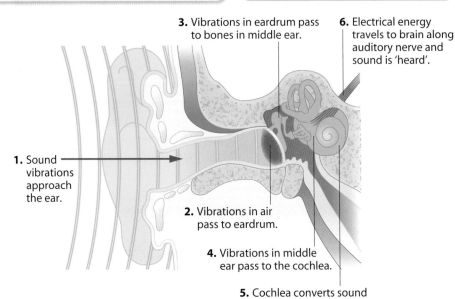

3. Vibrations in eardrum pass to bones in middle ear.

6. Electrical energy travels to brain along auditory nerve and sound is 'heard'.

1. Sound vibrations approach the ear.

2. Vibrations in air pass to eardrum.

4. Vibrations in middle ear pass to the cochlea.

5. Cochlea converts sound energy to electrical energy.

C *Energy is transferred through the ear.*

4 What is the main energy change that happens in the ear?

5 Which part of the ear:
a detects the sound waves
b sends signals to the brain

c passes the vibrations from the eardrum to the cochlea?

6 Draw a flow chart to show how energy is transferred through the ear. Ⓗ Ⓢ Ⓦ

Ear damage

The ear is very delicate. It contains thin membranes (thin layers of cells) and tiny bones, which are easily damaged.

- The ear can get blocked by wax and the eardrum cannot vibrate. A doctor can wash out the wax and cure the deafness caused.
- Accidents or a loud bang can damage the eardrum. This may repair itself.
- The middle ear can get infected. Ear infections can be treated by **antibiotics**.
- As people get older the tiny bones in their ears can fuse together and so don't vibrate.
- Sometimes the nerve cells in the cochlea do not work as well when you get older so the signals are not sent to the brain.
- The cochlea can be damaged by loud noise, for example from nightclubs or wearing personal stereos that are too loud. There is no cure for this.

7 Name three ways in which the ear can be damaged.

8 Think of a plus, minus and interesting point for these statements:
a A mouse should be able to hear sounds from a greater distance
b Humans should be able to hear much higher frequencies.

9 Midwives use a piece of equipment called a pinard. Explain how you think it works.

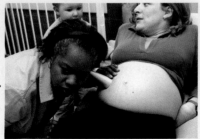
Ⓕ *A midwife using a pinard.*

Ⓓ *A hearing aid can be used to make sounds louder.*

People with poor hearing started using large hearing trumpets in the seventeenth century. The first electrical hearing aid was made in 1902 by American inventor Miller Reese Hutchison (1876–1944).

Ⓔ

I CAN...

- describe differences in the ranges of hearing of different animals.
- describe how vibrations travel through the ear.
- list some ways in which ear hearing loss can occur.

How do dolphins use sound?

In 1953 the underwater explorer Jacques Cousteau (1910–1997) observed that when his boat was heading along a deep channel in murky water, porpoises would follow. If he steered off course, the porpoises also steered off course but then quickly went back to following the channel. He thought that the porpoises could detect the channel (the best route to take) without being able to see it. Other scientists had also come up with this theory.

In 1960 Kenneth Norris (1924–1998) showed that this theory was correct. He put suction cups over the eyes of a dolphin and found that it could still find its way through a maze. Since then, many scientists have become interested in the different high-frequency 'clicks' and lower-frequency 'whistles' that these creatures make.

Today we know that dolphins produce clicks using nasal sacs. The sounds reflect off objects and are picked up again in the dolphin's lower jaw. The reflected sound waves travel through a channel filled with fat and then into the ear. Like light waves, sound waves can be focused, and dolphins have a 'lens' made of fat that they use to focus sound waves.

A This dolphin can easily find its way without being able to see.

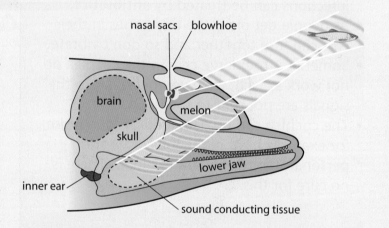

B How a dolphin's echolocation system works.

1. How did Norris' experiment show that dolphins did not need their eyes to navigate?
2. What do dolphins use to generate clicks?
3. Use diagram B to identify two ways in which light waves and sound waves are similar.
4. a What do you think dolphins use their fat 'lenses' for?
   b Why is this way of navigating and finding things called 'echolocation'?

Sound waves that have a frequency above 20 000 Hz (the upper limit of human hearing) are called **ultrasound**. Ultrasound waves are used in hospitals to look inside people – a so-called ultrasound scan, which most pregnant women have. Some dolphins seem to be able to find fish that are well-buried in sand and this has led some scientists to suggest that dolphins can also use ultrasound to see things in the same way that an ultrasound scanner does. However, dolphins are only known to emit sound waves with frequencies up to about 150 kHz whereas ultrasound machines use waves of 1–20 MHz.

5 What is ultrasound?

6 a What does Hz stand for?
   b Write out 150 kHz and 20 MHz in Hz.

7 a What is the evidence to suggest that dolphins can use ultrasound like an ultrasound scanner?
   b What is the evidence against this theory?

8 What advantage would there be if a dolphin could see inside a shark's stomach to find out if it was empty or full?

C *This dolphin has identified food buried deep under the sand, without being able to see it. Is it using ultrasound to do this?*

In 2006, a team from St Andrew's University recorded the whistles made by dolphins and played them back to the dolphins. They discovered that each dolphin had its own 'signature' whistle by which other dolphins recognised them. Whether dolphins actually have a language is the topic of a lot of research. Liz Hawkins, of the Whale Research Centre in Australia, spent three years listening to bottlenose dolphins and by 2007 had identified 186 different whistle types. Now she is trying to work out what they all mean!

This pack contains a microphone and recording equipment.

D *Michael Schotten, working with the Wild Dolphin Project, records dolphin sounds using four underwater microphones attached to a video camera. Other dolphins wear microphones and recording equipment. Using the video and the sound recordings, scientists are trying to work out if the dolphins are saying anything.*

9 The military have trained dolphins to find underwater objects like mines.
   a Why are dolphins good at finding objects like this?
   b Do you think they should be trained to do these sorts of jobs? Explain why you think this.

How is loudness measured?

When a sound wave hits an object it can be **reflected**. The wave bounces off the object and causes an **echo**.

Sound waves that do not get reflected by a material and do not pass through it are said to be **absorbed** by the material. Materials that are good absorbers of sound do not pass on vibrations to other particles. These materials are called '**sound insulators**'.

Scientists' knowledge of how sound is reflected and absorbed by different materials has allowed them to make important advances such as soundproofing and ultrasound.

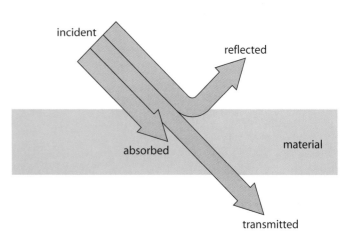

A Sound waves can be reflected off a material, absorbed by it or transmitted through it.

> 1 How can the reflection of sound be:
>   a useful   b annoying?
> 2 How is a sound insulator similar to and different from a heat insulator? **H S W**

B Soundproofing means that sound cannot enter or leave the recording area in a studio.

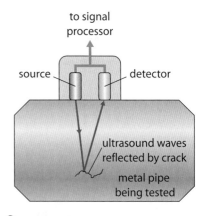

C Ultrasound can be used to check for flaws in metal structures.

Unwanted sound is called **noise**. Sounds that are very loud or unpleasant are classed as being 'noisy'.

We can measure how loud a sound is by using a **sound intensity meter**. This is an instrument which measures the loudness of a sound in **decibels (dB)**.

The **threshold of hearing** is the quietest sound we can hear. We call this 0 dB. The loudness of a road drill is 90 dB. This is the top limit of acceptable noise by law. A noisy factory can be louder than this. If you dance by the speakers in a nightclub, you can also hear sounds louder than 90 dB. Sound starts to become painful at about 134 dB and the eardrum breaks at 185 dB.

D A sound intensity meter being used.

3 a Use the decibel scale on the right to name three noisy animals.
 b Predict which of these noises might harm your hearing. Ⓗ Ⓢ Ⓦ

4 Use the decibel scale to name three artificial sound sources that could be harmful to your hearing.

5 What is the threshold of hearing?

Ⓗ Ⓢ Ⓦ

How could you find out which materials are the best sound insulators?
- What materials would you use?
- What equipment would you use to detect the sounds?
- How would you decide which material was the best sound insulator?

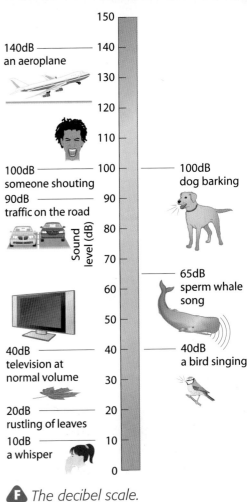

140dB
an aeroplane

100dB
someone shouting

90dB
traffic on the road

40dB
television at normal volume

20dB
rustling of leaves

10dB
a whisper

100dB
dog barking

65dB
sperm whale song

40dB
a bird singing

We know that animals can use sound to communicate and that they can also be very noisy. Some animals, however, do not like noise and like to live in a quiet environment.

Ⓕ *The decibel scale.*

Ⓖ *The tube running over this zoo contains a soundproofed motorway!*

6 How do you think the motorway in photo G is soundproofed?

7 How would nocturnal animals protect themselves from noise in the wild?

A device called the 'mosquito' is used in some parts of the UK to deter teenagers from lingering around certain areas. The device emits an ultra-high frequency sound wave that teenagers and people under the age of 25 can hear and find uncomfortable. Older people lose the ability to hear these high-pitched sounds and so are not affected.

8 Think of a plus, minus and interesting statement for:
 a All buildings should be soundproofed
 b Objects should not reflect sound waves. Ⓗ Ⓢ Ⓦ

9 Do you think the 'mosquito' is a good idea? Explain why you think this. Ⓗ Ⓢ Ⓦ

I CAN...

- explain how sound is reflected and absorbed.
- describe how soundproofing works.
- recall what noise is.
- describe how sound intensity is measured.

Ⓗ Ⓢ Ⓦ

8Le Sound developments

HowScienceWorks

Is studying animal communication useful?

Scientists know that animals use high and low frequency sounds to communicate, navigate, hunt and avoid capture.

Ships use 'sonar' to find out what is below them. The system produces sounds that reflect back to the ship, in the same way as bats. Whales use a similar system. Some think that sonar confuses the whales' system and can cause them to beach themselves. By researching whale hearing we could try to design sonar systems that don't cause beaching.

Scientists think that sperm whales use sound waves to stun and kill the giant squid that they feed on. If we research how they produce these sounds, we could make effective weapons against enemy divers.

Thanks to scientists working out the frequencies that animals can hear, I can use this ultrasonic device to keep cats out of my garden. If a cat walks in front of the device they are shocked by a sound that I can't hear.

In order to understand ourselves as humans, we need to understand through the lens or the mirror of another species that's very closely related to us, many aspects of our behaviour – Dr. Sue Savage-Rumbaugh.

1 Draw a diagram to show how the **sonar** system used by ships works.
2 The device in photo B has 'a frequency range of 21–25 kHz'.
   a Explain what this means.
   b Suggest one disadvantage of using this device.
3 Suggest how a weapon based on sounds would work. Use the word 'energy' in your answer.

HAVE YOUR SAY

Some people think that it is a waste of money to pay scientists to research into animal sounds and communication.
What do you think?

Glossary

Pronunciation note: A capital 'O' is said as in 'so'

absorbed (physics)	When energy is 'soaked up' or 'taken in'. If something absorbs light it soaks it up and does not let it back out.
absorbed (biology)	When small, soluble molecules go through the wall of the small intestine into the blood.
acid rain	Rain that is more acidic than usual because of chemicals dissolved in it.
adaptation (add-app-**tay**-shun)	The features of an organism that allow it to live in its environment.
adapted	When the features of an organism help it to survive in a habitat, it is adapted to that habitat.
aerobic (air-r**O**-bick)	With air.
aerobic respiration (ress-per-ay-shun)	Process that releases energy from digested food. Needs oxygen from the air. Carbon dioxide is produced as a waste gas.
AIDS	A disease caused by HIV – a virus that leads to the weakening of the immune system. Short for acquired immuno**d**eficiency syndrome.
ailerons	Flaps on the ends of an aeroplane's wing, that help to control it.
air resistance	A force trying to slow things that are moving through the air. It is a type of friction, and is sometimes called drag.
air sacs	Groups of alveoli in the lungs where oxygen comes out of the air and goes into the blood. Carbon dioxide is also transferred from the blood to the air in these.
alchemists (al-kem-ists)	Scientists (originally Arabic) who carried out the first experiments to make a range of new substances.
alloy	A metal with one or more other elements mixed in.
alveolus (al-vee-**O**-lus)	Small, round pocket that is grouped with other alveoli to form air sacs in the lungs. Plural = **alveoli**.
amphibian	Vertebrate with moist skin (e.g. frog).
amplitude	Half the height of a wave.
anaerobic	Means 'not requiring air' – or more properly 'not requiring oxygen from the air'.
anaerobic respiration	A form of respiration that does not use oxygen.
angle of incidence (in-sid-dense)	Angle between an incoming light ray and the normal.
angle of reflection	The angle between the normal and the ray of light leaving a mirror.
angle of refraction	Angle between the light ray and the normal as it passed from one transparent material into another.
animal kingdom	The group of organisms that contains all vertebrates and invertebrates.
antibiotic (ant-ee-by-**ot**-tick)	Medicine that can kill bacteria but not viruses.
antibody	Small chemicals made by some white blood cells. They attach to microbes and help to destroy them.
antiseptic	Weak disinfectant safe to use on human skin.
anus	The opening at the end of the gut.
aperture	The hole that light passes through to get inside a camera.
apparatus (app-ar-ay-tus)	The equipment used to carry out an experiment.
appendix	Small tube branching off the large intestine. It has no function in humans.
artery	Blood vessel that carries blood away from the heart.
arthropod (arth-row-pod)	Invertebrate that has jointed legs (e.g. fly, spider).
atom	The smallest part of an element.
attract	Two things pulling towards each other.
bacterium	A type of microbe bigger than viruses. (plural = **bacteria**)

balanced diet	Eating a wide variety of foods to give us all the things that we need.
balanced forces	Equal forces working in opposite directions on an object.
bar magnet	A straight magnet shaped like a small bar.
basalt (ba-salt)	An igneous rock with very tiny crystals.
bauxite (bork-site)	Mineral (ore) that contains aluminium oxide – the main source of aluminium.
behaviour	The way an organism acts or reacts to things around it.
benefit	An improvement caused by something.
biceps muscle	The muscle on the front of the upper arm that makes the arm bend.
biological weathering	When rocks are broken down due to the activities of living things (e.g. growing plant roots can split rocks apart).
bird	Vertebrate with feathers (e.g. eagle).
blood	Contains cells and a liquid called plasma. It flows around the body carrying various substances which are either made by the body or needed by the body.
blood vessel	Tubes in which blood flows. There are capillaries, veins and arteries.
boiling point	When a liquid is at its boiling point it is as hot as it can get. It is evaporating as fast as it can.
bonds	Forces holding particles together.
breathing	Moving muscles in order to make air flow into and out of the lungs.
breathing rate	The number of times you breathe in one minute.
breathing system	Set of organs (lungs, windpipe, diaphragm) that allow air to be taken into and out of the body. Also called the respiratory system.
brine	A solution of common salt and water.
bronchus	Tube in the lungs that connects the windpipe to the air sacs. Plural = **bronchi**.
budding	The way yeast cells divide. A new small cell (a bud) starts to grow out from another cell.
camera	A box that lets light through a hole in one side to form an image.
capillaries (cap-ill-arr-ees)	The smallest blood vessels. Substances enter and leave the blood through the thin walls of capillaries.
carbohydrate (car-b**O**-**high**-drate)	Nutrient that is used as the main source of energy.
carbon dioxide	A product of respiration.
catastrophism (kat-a-**strof**-ism)	The theory that all the rocks were formed by sudden events such as volcanic eruptions.
CCD	Stands for 'charge coupled device'. The device in a digital camera that converts light into electrical signals.
cementation (sem-men-**tay**-shun)	A process in which water is squeezed out of the spaces between pieces of rock leaving mineral salts behind which stick (cement) the rock pieces together.
cements (sem-**men**-ts)	Sticks.
chalk	A soft white or grey sedimentary rock formed from the remains of microscopic organisms, and so mainly made out of calcium carbonate.
chamber	The heart contains four compartments called chambers.
characteristics	The features of an organism.
chemical change	A change which forms one or more new substances.
chemical energy	The kind of energy stored in chemicals. Food, fuels and electrical cells all contain chemical energy.

chemical formula	A combination of symbols and numbers that shows how many atoms of different kinds are in a particular molecule. In compounds that do not form molecules, it shows the ratio of elements in the compound.
chemical weathering	When rocks are broken up or dissolved by chemical reactions, usually with rainwater.
chromatogram	A dried piece of paper produced by chromatography.
chromatography	Separating dissolved solids from one another. The solids are usually coloured.
chromosome (*crow-mow-sowm*)	String-like threads contained in the nucleus of a cell. Chromosomes contain DNA which contains the instructions for inherited variations.
cilia (*sil-lee-a*)	Small hairs on the surface of some cells.
ciliated epithelial cell (*sil-lee-ay-ted eppy-theel-ee-al*)	Cells in the trachea that have microscopic hairs (cilia) growing from them, which wave to move mucus up to the gullet to be swallowed.
circulatory system	System containing the heart and blood vessels.
classification (*clas-if-ik-ay-shun*)	Sorting things into groups.
classified	Placing things in their groups according to their characteristics.
classify	Placing things in their groups according to their characteristics.
clear	See-through or transparent.
clot	When blood becomes solid. Makes a 'scab' when it is on the surface of the skin.
cobalt (*cO-balt*)	A metal that is a magnetic material.
cochlea (*cok-lee-a*)	The part of the ear that changes vibrations into electrical impulses.
colourless	Something which has no colour.
common salt	A chemical we use to make things taste 'salty'.
community (*com-mew-nit-ee*)	All the plants and animals that live in a habitat.
compaction (*com-pack-shun*)	When layers of sediment or rock are squashed by the weight of sediment above them.
compass	A magnetised piece of metal that can swing around – one end always points north.
compete	All organisms need some of the same things and so each organism has to try to get these things before another organism does. For example, plants compete with one another for light.
competition (*comp-pet-tish-un*)	Organisms may compete with each other for food, light and space in a habitat.
compounds	Substances that can be split up into simpler substances.
computer modelling	Using computers to estimate how things have changed in the past and how they will continue to change.
concave	A lens that is fatter at the ends or edges than in the middle.
concentrated	A chemical that is concentrated has lots of the chemical in a small volume.
condense	When a gas turns into a liquid.
conduction (*con-duck-shun*)	The way heat travels through solids.
conductor	A material which lets energy flow through it easily.
cone	Something used to carry the seeds of conifers.
conifer	Plant with needle-shaped leaves. Reproduces using seeds found in cones.
constipation (*con-stip-ay-shun*)	When the intestines get blocked up.
constructive plate margin	Where two plates are moving apart and new rock is being formed in the gap.
consumer	An organism that has to eat other organisms to stay alive. Animals are consumers.
continental crust	The crust that forms the continents. It is less dense than oceanic crust.
continental drift	The theory that pieces of the Earth's crust moved through the rocks beneath the ocean.

contract	To get smaller.
convection	The transfer of heat in fluids.
convection current	A current created by heat causing changes in the density of a fluid.
converging lens	A lens that makes rays of light come together. Another name for a convex lens.
convex	A lens that is fatter in the middle than at the ends or edges.
core (chemistry)	The middle of the Earth.
core (physics)	A solid bar inside an electromagnet – usually made of iron.
creationism (*kree-ay-shun-ism*)	The idea that the world was created by God in six days, as described in the Bible.
crust	The solid rocks at the surface of the Earth.
crystal (*kris-tal*)	Piece of mineral with sharp edges.
cuticle	Layer of cells on leaves that is waterproof.
cyan (*sye-an*)	Secondary colour made by mixing green and blue light (greeny blue).
cycles per second	The number of complete backwards and forwards vibrations made in one second.
data	The observations from an experiment.
decibel (dB) (*dess-i-bell*)	Unit for measuring the loudness of a sound.
decompose	Break down into simpler parts.
degrees Celsius (°C) (*sell-see-us*)	The units for measuring temperature.
deposit	When moving air, water or ice drops rock fragments or grains it has been carrying.
destructive plate margin	Where two plates meet and one is being pushed down under the other.
diabetes (*dye-ab-eet-eez*)	Disease in which the levels of glucose in the blood cannot be controlled.
diagnosis	What a doctor thinks is causing a person's symptoms.
diaphragm (*dye-aff-ram*)	Sheet of muscle under the lungs. When it moves down your lungs get bigger.
diet	The food that you eat.
diffusion (*diff-you-shun*)	The natural movement of particles from a place where there are a lot of them to a place where there are fewer of them.
digested	Broken down into smaller pieces.
digestion (*dye-jes-jun*)	Process that breaks food into soluble substances in our bodies.
digestive juice	A liquid containing enzymes that break down food.
digestive system	The group of organs that carry out digestion.
digital camera	A camera that uses electronics (instead of film) to record an image.
disease	When some processes that happen in the body do not work in the way they should.
disinfectant	Strong chemical used to kill microbes.
dispersion	The separating of the colours in light, for example when white light passes through a prism.
dissolving (*diss-olv-ing*)	When a solid splits up and mixes with a liquid to make a solution.
distance multiplier	A lever where the load moves further than the effort.
distillation	The process of separating a liquid from a solution by evaporating the liquid and then condensing it.
distribution (*diss-trib-you-shun*)	The places where an organism can be found in a habitat.
diverging lens	A lens that makes rays of light spread out.
drag	Air resistance and water resistance are both sometimes called drag.
ductile	Able to be stretched into a thin wire.
eardrum	A thin membrane inside the ear which vibrates when sound reaches it.
earthquake	When the earth shakes.
echinoderm (*ek-eye-no-derm*)	Invertebrate with body in five parts, e.g. starfish.

echo (eck-O)	Sound reflected back from something solid.
ecologist	A person who studies the environment.
effort	The force put on something, especially a lever.
egestion (ee-jes-jun)	When faeces are pushed out of the anus.
electrical conductor	Something which allows electricity to flow through it easily.
electrodes	Solid conductors of electricity attached to a power supply in electrolysis.
electrolysis (e-leck-troll-ee-sis)	Passing electricity through a compound when it is molten or in solution to break it down.
electromagnet	A coil of wire with electricity flowing in it. An electromagnet has a magnetic field like a bar magnet.
electroplating	Putting a thin metal coating onto another metal.
element	A substance that cannot be split up into anything simpler by chemical reactions. All the atoms in an element are the same.
elevator	A flap on the tailplane of an aeroplane that helps to control it.
emit	To give out energy.
emphysema	A disease in which the lungs cannot take much oxygen out of the air.
endangered	A species which is at risk of becoming extinct.
engulf	When a white blood cell completely surrounds a microbe and destroys it, it is said to engulf the microbe.
environment	The conditions around an organism caused by physical environmental factors.
environmental factors	Things in an environment that can change something about an organism.
enzyme	A chemical that can break up large molecules.
erosion (er-O-shun)	The movement of loose and weathered rock.
estimate	Provide a rough idea about the numbers of something or the size of something.
ethanol	Often just called 'alcohol'. Produced by yeasts when they ferment sugar.
evaporate	When a liquid turns into a gas.
evidence (ev-i-dense)	Information that helps to prove that an idea is correct or incorrect.
excrete	To get rid of waste products from the body.
exhale	To breathe out.
exhaled air	Air that is breathed out.
exoskeleton (ex-O-skel-e-ton)	Thick outer covering found in arthropods.
expand	Get bigger.
exposure	The amount of light let into a camera when taking a photograph.
extinct	A species that no longer exists.
faeces (fee-sees)	Waste food material produced by the intestines.
fat	Nutrient that is stored to be used for energy in the future. It also helps to keep heat in our bodies.
feeding relationship	A description of how an organism feeds on others.
fermentation	The type of anaerobic respiration carried out by yeasts. It produces carbon dioxide and ethanol.
fern	Plant that has many small waterproof leaves. Reproduces using spores.
fever	A high body temperature.
fibre (fie-ber)	Substance found in food that cannot be used by the body. It helps to keep our intestines clean.
film	A thin sheet of plastic coated with chemicals that change when light hits them. It is used in some cameras to record images.
filter (physics)	Something which only lets certain colours through and absorbs the rest.
filtering (chemistry)	Separating things that have not dissolved from a liquid. The liquid is passed through a filter (such as filter paper) to do this.
filtrate	The liquid that runs through filter paper.
fin	The vertical part of the tail of an aeroplane.

fish	Vertebrate with wet scales, e.g. salmon.
flagellum (flaj-ell-um)	Tail on, for example, a bacterium. (plural = flagellae)
flowering plant	Plant with large, flat leaves. Reproduces using seeds found in fruits. Fruits and seeds form inside flowers.
fluid	A gas or a liquid.
focus	To adjust a camera so that the picture will be sharp and clear.
food web	Many food chains linked together.
force multiplier	A lever where the load is bigger than the effort.
fossil	The remains of a dead animal or plant that became trapped in layers of sediment and turned into rock.
freezing point	The temperature at which a liquid turns into a solid. It is the same temperature as the melting point of the substance.
frequency (free-kwen-see)	The number of waves each second.
fruit	Something used to carry the seeds of flowering plants. Can be fleshy or dry.
fulcrum	A point about which something turns. Another name for a pivot.
fungus	Organism which is different from animals, plants and bacteria. Examples include mushrooms and yeasts. (plural = fungi)
gas exchange	Taking oxygen into the blood and getting rid of carbon dioxide into the lungs. Happens in the air sacs in the lungs.
geologist	A scientist who studies rocks and the Earth.
gill	A series of flaps of tissue with a good blood supply just behind the head of an organism which is used to take oxygen out of the water. Fish have gills.
global warming	The theory that certain gases in the atmosphere are causing it to get hotter.
glucose	A type of sugar.
gneiss (nice)	A metamorphic rock formed when schist is heated and squashed more. It usually has bands of different coloured minerals.
grain	Tiny piece of rock.
granite (gran-it)	An igneous rock with large crystals.
guideway	The 'track' that a maglev train runs on.
gullet	Tube that goes from the mouth to the stomach. Sometimes called the 'food pipe'.
gut	All the organs of the digestive system apart from the mouth.
habitat	The place an organism lives in (e.g. woodland).
hard water	Water with certain chemicals dissolved in it that cause scum and stop soap making a lather.
health claim	Statement telling you about a food's good effects on your body.
heart	Organ that pumps blood around the body.
heart attack	When the heart stops pumping.
heart disease	Disease caused by narrowing of the arteries carrying the blood to the muscles of the heart, so the heart muscles do not receive enough oxygen.
heartbeat	One pump of the heart.
heat	A form of energy, measured in joules.
heat conductor	Something which allows heat to flow through it easily.
hertz (Hz)	The unit for frequency. 1 hertz means one wave per second.
high melting point	Something with a high melting point has to be at a very high temperature before it melts. It is a solid at room temperature.
HIV	A virus that causes AIDS. Stands for human immunodeficiency virus.
HIV-positive	Someone who has HIV in their body is described as being HIV-positive.
humidity	The amount of water vapour in the air.

hydrogencarbonate indicator	An indicator that can be used to show how much carbon dioxide there is in something.
igneous rock (igg-nee-us)	A rock formed when magma or lava cooled down and solidified.
image	A picture which forms in a mirror, or on a screen, or is made by lenses.
immune (imm-you'n)	If you cannot get a disease you are said to be 'immune' to it.
immunisation (imm-you'n-eyes-ay-shun)	Making people immune to diseases.
impulse	Electrical signal carried by a nerve cell.
incident ray (in-sid-dent)	Light ray hitting a mirror or other object.
indicator	A chemical that changes colour depending on how acidic or alkaline a liquid is.
infect	When a microbe gets into your body you are 'infected' by it.
infectious (in-feck-shus)	A disease that can be spread from person to person or from animal to person is infectious.
infrared	A 'colour' of light beyond red. We can feel this as heat but we cannot see it.
infrared radiation	Another name for heat energy that travels by radiation. It can travel through transparent things and a vacuum (empty space).
ingestion (in-jes-jun)	Putting food into your mouth.
inhale	To breathe in.
inhaled air	Air that is breathed in.
inherited characteristics	Characteristics we receive from our parents.
inherited variation	Differences between organisms passed to offspring by their parents in reproduction.
innate	Behaviour that happens automatically and does not need to be learned.
insecticide	Poison used to kill insects.
insoluble	Something that does not dissolve is said to be insoluble.
insulator	A material which does not let energy flow through it easily.
insulin (in-syou-lin)	A chemical made in the pancreas that causes cells to take glucose out of the blood.
intensity	The loudness or volume of a sound.
interface	The boundary between two materials.
invertebrate (in-vert-eb-rate)	Animal without a backbone.
investigate (in-ves-ti-gate)	To find out about something and test a theory.
iris	The coloured part of the eye. This controls the size of the pupil.
iron	A metal that is a magnetic material.
iron filings (f'eye-lings)	Tiny pieces of iron that are sometimes used to find the shape of a magnetic field.
joule (J)	The units for measuring energy.
kilojoule (kJ) (kill-O-jool)	Unit of energy used on food packets. There are 1000J in 1kJ.
kingdoms	Largest groups that living things are sorted into. The two biggest are the plant kingdom and the animal kingdom.
large intestine	Organ that takes water out of waste food.
laser (lay-zer)	Something which produces a narrow beam of light of one pure colour (short for Light Amplification by Stimulated Emission of Radiation).
lava (lar-va)	Molten rock that runs out of volcanoes.
learned behaviour	Behaviour (what an organism does) that is learned and not automatic.
lens	A curved piece of glass or other transparent material that can bend rays of light.
lever	A simple machine that can increase the size of a force, or increase the distance the force moves.
levitate	To rise up.

limestone	A sedimentary rock made from the shells of dead sea creatures.
limiting factor	Something that stops a population growing.
liver	Organ that makes and destroys many substances in the body.
living factor	An organism in a habitat that affects other organisms in the habitat.
load	The weight or force on something.
loudness	How loud a sound is; the volume of a sound.
low boiling point	Something with a low boiling point will turn into a gas at a relatively low temperature. It can be a solid, liquid or gas at room temperature.
low melting point	Something with a low melting point turns into a liquid at a relatively low temperature. It can be a solid, liquid or gas at room temperature.
luminous sources (loo-min-us)	Objects that create light.
magenta (ma-jen-ta)	Secondary colour made by mixing red and blue light (pinkish red).
maglev	Trains that use electromagnets to make them float (or levitate) above the tracks and move along are called maglev trains.
magma	Molten rock beneath the surface of the Earth.
magnet	Something that can attract magnetic materials.
magnetic	A metal (steel, iron, nickel or cobalt) that can be magnetised or attracted to a magnet.
magnetic field	The space around a magnet where it can affect magnetic materials or other magnets.
magnetic materials	Materials that are attracted to a magnet; iron, cobalt, nickel and steel are all magnetic materials.
magnetism	A non-contact force caused by magnets.
malleable	Able to be easily hammered into different shapes.
mammal	Vertebrate that has hair and produces milk (e.g. human).
mantle (man-tel)	The part of the Earth below the crust.
marble	A metamorphic rock formed from limestone.
medicine	A drug that helps the body to ease the symptoms of a disease or cure the disease.
medium	Any substance.
melt	When a solid turns into a liquid.
melting point	The temperature at which a solid turns into a liquid. It is the same temperature as the freezing point of the substance.
metals	Elements that are shiny, conduct heat and electricity well, and often have high melting and boiling points.
metamorphic rock (met-a-mor-fik)	Rocks that have been formed by changing igneous or sedimentary rocks.
microbe	A very small living thing. Also called a micro-organism.
micro-organism	A very small living thing.
migration	When animals move out of an area (usually when resources become scarce).
mineral	Properly called a 'mineral salt', an element or compound found naturally in rocks and soil. It is a nutrient needed in small quantities for health (e.g. calcium).
mixture	Two or more different substances that are not joined to each other.
model	Way of thinking about something and imagining what it is like and how it works. It can allow you to more easily think about how a complicated thing works.
molecule	Two or more atoms joined together.
mollusc	Invertebrate with a large fleshy muscle that it uses to feed or move, e.g. snail.
moss	Plant with many thin leaves but without roots and xylem. Reproduces using spores.

mucus (*mew*-cus)	Slimy substance found in nose and trachea that traps dirt and microbes and is moved out of the lungs by cilia.
mudstone	A sedimentary rock made of tiny particles.
natural defences	Your body's way of trying to keep microbes out (e.g. skin) or killing them if they get inside you (e.g. stomach acid).
nickel	A metal that is a magnetic material.
noise	Unpleasant sound.
non-contact force	A force, such as magnetism or gravity, that does not need to be touching something to have an effect.
non-luminous	Objects that do not create light.
non-metals	Elements that are not shiny, and do not conduct heat and electricity well.
normal	An imaginary line at right angles to the surface of a mirror or other object, where a ray of light hits it.
north magnetic pole	The place on the Earth where compasses point (it is not in the same place as the North Pole marked on maps).
north pole	One end of a magnet. This end points north if the magnet can move. Sometimes called the 'north-seeking pole'.
north-seeking pole	The end of a magnet that points north if the magnet can move freely. Often just called the north pole.
nutrient (*new*-tree-ent)	Substance needed in the diet to provide raw materials.
nutrition information (new-*trish*-un)	Information label found on a food packet to tell you what is in the food.
obese	Being very overweight.
observations (ob-ser-*vay*-shuns)	Looking carefully at things and recording what you see or measure.
oceanic crust	The crust that forms the ocean floors. It is mostly basalt, and is more dense than continental crust.
opaque (*O*-pake)	Material which does not let light through.
optical fibre (*fie*-ber)	Long strand made of glass. Light travels down optical fibres because it is reflected from the inside surface of the fibre.
organism	A living thing.
oscilloscope (oss-*ill*-O-skope)	An instrument which shows a picture of a wave on a screen.
oxide	A compound that includes oxygen.
oxygen debt	The amount of oxygen needed to break down all the extra lactic acid after hard exercise.
pancreas	An organ that produces insulin and produces enzymes (which help to break down food).
particle theory	Otherwise known as the particle model of matter. Theory that says that all materials are made out of particles that are constantly moving.
particles	The tiny pieces that everything is made out of.
pascal (Pa)	A unit for pressure. $1 \text{ Pa} = 1 \text{ N/m}^2$.
pasteurisation (pas-ter-*eyes*-ay-shun)	Milk is heated up to 70°C for about 15 seconds, which is enough to kill the most harmful bacteria in it.
periodic table (peer-ee-*od*-ick)	Table that shows all the elements, arranged in a regular order to show patterns in properties.
permanent magnet	A magnet that keeps its magnetism – it does not depend on electricity.
persistent chemical	A chemical that does not get broken down in nature very quickly. It stays around for a long time.
pesticide (pest-*iss*-ide)	Chemical that kills pests.
pests	Organism that damages crops.
photosynthesis (foto-*sinth*-e-sis)	Process that plants use to make their own food. It needs light to work. Carbon dioxide and water are the reactants. Food (a sugar called glucose) and oxygen are the products.
physical change (*fizz*-ick-al)	A change where no new substances are formed.

physical environmental factors	The non-living conditions in the environment of an organism (e.g. temperature, light).
physical weathering	When rocks are broken up by physical processes such as changes in temperature.
pinhole camera	Something that forms an image of an object when light rays travel through a tiny hole in the front.
pitch	How high or low a note sounds.
pitfall trap	Sampling method used to collect small animals that live on the ground.
pivot	Another name for a fulcrum.
plane	Smooth and flat.
plane mirror	Smooth, flat mirror.
plant kingdom	Group of organisms that are able to produce their own food using photosynthesis.
plasma	Part of the blood. A liquid that surrounds the blood cells.
plate tectonics	The modern theory that the Earth's crust is split into separate plates which can move around.
plates	Pieces of the surface of the Earth, which can move around very slowly.
plotting compass	A small compass used for finding the direction of a magnetic field.
pond dipping	Sampling method used to collect organisms from ponds.
pooter	A small container connected to two tubes. Used to catch tiny animals.
population	Total number of individuals of the same species in a habitat.
precipitate (pres-*sip*-it-tate)	Insoluble solid produced by mixing two solutions.
precipitation	Chemical reaction which forms a solid by mixing two solutions.
predator	An animal that catches and eats other animals.
predict	When you have an idea about what will happen when you change something.
prediction (pred-*ick*-shun)	An idea about what will happen when you change something.
pressure	A way of saying how spread out a force is. Pressure in liquids and gases is the force caused by particles hitting a certain area.
prey (*pray*)	An animal that is caught and eaten by another animal.
primary colours	The three main colours which can make white light (red, green and blue).
primary consumer	The first animal in a food chain.
prism	A block of clear, colourless glass or plastic, which is usually triangular.
producer	An organism that is able to make its own food.
product	New chemical formed in a chemical reaction.
properties	Ways of describing a substance.
propulsion	A way of making something move.
protein	Nutrient used for growth and repair.
protein coat	The outer covering of a virus particle is made of protein and so is called a protein coat.
pulse	The feel of your blood being pumped.
pulse rate	The number of times you can feel your blood being pumped in 1 minute.
pupil	The gap in the front of the eye that light can pass through.
pure	A substance that does not have anything else in it.
pyramid of numbers	Way of showing the numbers of different organisms in a food chain.
quadrat	A square frame, thrown randomly on the ground, which is used to sample the plants in an area.
quality standards	Rules about how pure something has to be. For water, the standards state the amount of salt and micro-organisms that are allowed to be in drinking water.

quartz	The mineral that forms the grains in sandstone.
quartzite (kwartz-ite)	A metamorphic rock formed from sandstone.
radiation	The transfer of heat energy by waves.
radius bone	The bone between the elbow and the wrist that the biceps muscle pulls on.
raw materials	Substances used to make other substances out of.
ray	A beam of light drawn on diagrams as a straight line, and showing which way it is travelling.
ray diagram	A diagram showing the passage of light rays.
reactant	Chemical that is used up in a chemical reaction.
recommended daily allowance (RDA)	The amount of a nutrient that it is recommended you have in your food each day.
rectum	Organ that stores faeces before they are egested.
recycling (ree-sy-cling)	Using a material again, often by melting it and using it to make new objects.
red blood cells	Cells in the blood that carry oxygen.
reflect	Light bounces back from a surface instead of passing through it.
reflected ray	The ray of light bouncing off a mirror.
reflection	Light bouncing back from a surface instead of passing through it.
refracted	The ray of light bending when it goes from one substance to another.
refraction	The change in direction when light goes from one transparent material to another.
renewable	A material or energy source that will not run out.
repel	Push away.
replicate	Viruses cannot reproduce on their own. They use the cell that they have infected to help them make new copies of the virus. We say that the virus particles replicate.
replication	The process that happens when a cell makes new copies of a virus.
reptile	Vertebrate with dry scales (e.g. snake).
residue	The solid bits that are trapped by filter paper.
resistant	Something that is not affected by a disease is said to be resistant to it.
resources	Things that an organism needs in order to survive in a habitat (e.g. a source of food).
respiration (ress-per-ay-shun)	Process that uses up oxygen to release energy from food. Carbon dioxide is produced as a waste gas.
respiratory system	Set of organs (lungs, windpipe, diaphragm) that allow air to be taken into and out of the body. Also called the breathing system.
retina	The part inside the eye that converts light into electrical signals.
re-use	When an object is used again, without being broken up or recycled.
rock cycle	All the processes which form sedimentary, igneous and metamorphic rocks linked together.
rock salt	Salt that is found mixed with rock.
root	Plant organ used to take water out of the soil.
rudder	A flap at the back of an aeroplane or ship that can be used to make it turn.
saliva (sall-eye-va)	A digestive juice. It contains an enzyme that breaks down starch into sugar.
salivary gland (sall-eye-vor-ee)	Found in the mouth. It makes saliva.
salts	Chemicals from rocks that have dissolved in water.
sample	A small part of something. If you sample something you take a small part of it. You use your results from the small part to suggest what the rest of it is like.
saturated	A solution that contains as much dissolved solid as is possibly can.
scab	A dry blood clot on the surface of the skin.
scatter	Spread out in all directions.

schist (shist)	A metamorphic rock formed when slate is heated and squashed more.
secondary colours	The colours made when two primary colours mix.
secondary consumer	The second animal in a food chain.
sediment	Rock grains and fragments dropped on the bottom or a river, lake or sea.
sedimentary rock	Rock formed from layers of sediment. It is often porous and made of rounded grains.
seeds	Grow into new plants. Made by conifers and flowering plants.
sensor	An instrument that detects something. In a digital camera, the sensors detect light and convert it to electrical signals.
septum	The part of the heart that separates the chambers on the right from the chambers on the left.
shadow	A place where light cannot get to, because an opaque object is stopping the light.
shiny	Reflects light well.
shutter	Part of a camera that stops light getting in except for when a photograph is being taken.
slate	A metamorphic rock with tiny crystals that are lined up. It is formed from mudstone, and can be split into layers.
small intestine	Organ where most digestion happens. The soluble substances produced by digestion are absorbed into the body here. It is about 6.5 m long in adults.
soft water	Water that is without the chemicals in hard water.
solubility (soll-you-bill-ity)	The amount of solid that will dissolve in 100 g of a liquid.
soluble (sol-you-ball)	Something that is soluble can dissolve in a liquid.
solute	The solid that has dissolved in a liquid to make a solution.
solution (sol-oo-shun)	When a solid has dissolved in a liquid.
solvent	The liquid that has dissolved a solid to make a solution.
sonar (sO-nar)	A machine for finding the depth of the sea or for finding fish by sending sound waves and listening for the echoes.
sound barrier	The speed of sound; people used to think that it would be impossible to travel faster than the speed of sound.
sound insulator	Material that is good at absorbing sound.
sound intensity meter	A meter which measures the loudness of a sound.
sound waves	Sound energy carried from one place to another in the form of waves.
source	An object that releases a form of energy.
south magnetic pole	The place near the south pole of the Earth that the south-seeking end of a magnet will point to.
south pole	One end of a magnet. This end points south if the magnet can move. Sometimes called the 'south-seeking pole'.
south-seeking pole	The end of a magnet that points south if the magnet can move freely. Often just called the south pole.
species (spee-shees)	A group of organisms that can reproduce with each other to produce offspring that will also be able to reproduce.
spectrum	The seven colours of light.
spore	Very small part of a plant that can grow into a new plant. Made by mosses and ferns.
starch	Type of insoluble carbohydrate found in plants.
starter culture	Small amount of actively growing microbe that is added to a mixture to grow large amounts of microbes.
steam	Water as a gas. Also called **water vapour**.
steel	A mixture made mainly from iron; it is a magnetic material.
stimulus	An event that causes something to happen.
still	The apparatus used for distillation.

stomach (stum-uck)	Organ containing strong acid that mixes food up and digests proteins.
strand of genes	A length of DNA that contains genes.
streamlined	Something that has a smooth shape to reduce the air resistance or water resistance.
sugar	Type of soluble carbohydrate. Glucose is an example of a sugar.
sustainable (sus-tane-a-bull)	A process that can be carried on for ever without running out of resources.
sweepnet	Sampling method used to collect small animals from long grass.
symbol	The letter or letters that represent an element.
symptoms	The effects that a disease has on your body.
T4 lymphocyte (lim-fow-site)	A type of white blood cell that helps to fight off infections.
tailplane	The horizontal surfaces at the rear of an aeroplane.
temperature	How hot something is, measured in °C.
tertiary consumer (tersh-ary)	The third animal in a food chain.
theory (theer-ree)	A scientific idea that can be tested.
thermal conductor	Another word for a heat conductor.
thermal energy	Another name for heat energy.
threshold of hearing	The quietest sound that can be heard.
tissue	A group of cells of the same type all doing the same job.
tissue fluid	The liquid formed when plasma leaks out of capillaries, carrying oxygen and food to cells.
top predator	The last animal in a food chain.
total internal reflection	When light is reflected inside a piece of glass or other transparent material.
toxic	Another word for poisonous.
trace	The wave that is shown on an oscilloscope screen.
trachea	Tube carrying air into and out of the lungs. Also called the windpipe.
transferred	Moving between two objects.
translucent (trans-loo-sent)	Material through which a glow of light can be seen.
transmit	To send along or pass through.
transparent	Material which light can travel through.
transport	The movement of rock grains and fragments by wind, water or ice.
tree beating	Sampling method used to collect animals from trees and bushes.
trend	A pattern found in data.
Tullgren funnel	Sampling method used to collect small animals from samples of, for example, leaves.
ultrasound	Sound that has a frequency too high for humans to hear.
ultraviolet	A 'colour' of light beyond violet. We cannot see ultraviolet light, but some animals (such as insects) can.
unbalanced forces	When two forces are not equal and opposite to each other.
uneven distribution	When a plant or animal is not found all over a habitat, only in certain places where the habitat is suitable.
uniformitarianism (yoo-nee-form-it-air-ee-an-ism)	The idea that rocks were formed over many millions of years by the same processes that we see happening today.
Unreactive	Difficult to get to react to other material.
vaccine (vack-seen)	A mixture containing microbes that normally cause disease, which have been treated so that they don't. Injected into people to make them immune.
vacuum	A completely empty space with no particles.
variable	A factor which can change or be changed in an experiment.
variation	The differences between things.

vein (vane)	Blood vessel that carries blood to the heart.
ventilation	Air moving into and out of the lungs.
vertebrate (vert-eb-rate)	Animal with a backbone.
vibrate	Move backwards and forwards.
viewfinder	Part of a camera that you look through to make sure you get the right things in the photograph.
villi (vill-ee)	Small finger-like parts of the small intestine. They increase the surface area so that digested food is absorbed more quickly. Singular = villus.
virus	The smallest type of microbe. Many people think that they are not living because they do not carry out the seven life processes for themselves.
vitamin	Nutrient needed in small quantities for health (e.g. vitamin C).
volcano	A mountain that shoots out molten rock.
volume	The loudness of a sound.
water resistance	A force that tries to slow things down that are moving through water. It is a type of friction, and is sometimes called drag.
water vapour	Water as a gas. Also called **steam**.
wave	A way of transferring energy. Light and sound both travel as waves.
wavelength	The distance between the top of one wave and the top of the next.
weathering	When rocks are broken up by physical, chemical or biological processes.
white blood cell	A type of blood cell which helps to destroy microbes. They either engulf microbes or make antibodies.
white light	Normal daylight, or the light from light bulbs, is white light.
windpipe	Tube carrying air into and out of the lungs. Also called the trachea.
word equation	A way of writing out what happens in a chemical reaction.
xylem vessel	A tissue made of hollow xylem cells joined end to end, which transports water through a plant.
yeast	A type of fungus with only one cell and therefore a microbe. Yeasts are bigger than bacteria.

The periodic table

Legend: metal / semi metal / non-metal

1	2											13	14	15	16	17	18
H 1 hydrogen																	**He** 2 helium
Li 3 lithium	**Be** 4 beryllium											**B** 5 boron	**C** 6 carbon	**N** 7 nitrogen	**O** 8 oxygen	**F** 9 fluorine	**Ne** 10 neon
Na 11 sodium	**Mg** 12 magnesium											**Al** 13 aluminium	**Si** 14 silicon	**P** 15 phosphorus	**S** 16 sulphur	**Cl** 17 chlorine	**Ar** 18 argon
K 19 potassium	**Ca** 20 calcium	**Sc** 21 scandium	**Ti** 22 titanium	**V** 23 vanadium	**Cr** 24 chromium	**Mn** 25 manganese	**Fe** 26 iron	**Co** 27 cobalt	**Ni** 28 nickel	**Cu** 29 copper	**Zn** 30 zinc	**Ga** 31 gallium	**Ge** 32 germanium	**As** 33 arsenic	**Se** 34 selenium	**Br** 35 bromine	**Kr** 36 krypton
Rb 37 rubidium	**Sr** 38 strontium	**Y** 39 yttrium	**Zr** 40 zirconium	**Nb** 41 niobium	**Mo** 42 molybdenum	**Tc** 43 technetium	**Ru** 44 ruthenium	**Rh** 45 rhodium	**Pd** 46 palladium	**Ag** 47 silver	**Cd** 48 cadmium	**In** 49 indium	**Sn** 50 tin	**Sb** 51 antimony	**Te** 52 tellurium	**I** 53 iodine	**Xe** 54 xenon
Cs 55 caesium	**Ba** 56 barium	**La** 57 lanthanum	**Hf** 72 hafnium	**Ta** 73 tantalum	**W** 74 tungsten	**Re** 75 rhenium	**Os** 76 osmium	**Ir** 77 iridium	**Pt** 78 platinum	**Au** 79 gold	**Hg** 80 mercury	**Tl** 81 thallium	**Pb** 82 lead	**Bi** 83 bismuth	**Po** 84 polonium	**At** 85 astatine	**Rn** 86 radon
Fr 87 francium	**Ra** 88 radium	**Ac** 89 actinium	**Rf** 104 rutherfordium	**Db** 105 dubnium	**Sg** 106 seaborgium	**Bh** 107 bohrium	**Hs** 108 hassium	**Mt** 109 meitnerium	**Ds** 110 damstadtium	**Rg** 111 roentgenium	**Uub** 112 ununbium	**Uut** 113 ununtrium	**Uuq** 114 ununquadium	**Uup** 115 ununpentium	**Uuh** 116 ununhexium		**Uuo** 118 ununoctium

Lanthanides:

Ce 58 cerium	**Pr** 59 praseodymium	**Nd** 60 neodymium	**Pm** 61 promethium	**Sm** 62 samarium	**Eu** 63 europium	**Gd** 64 gadolinium	**Tb** 65 terbium	**Dy** 66 dysprosium	**Ho** 67 holmium	**Er** 68 erbium	**Tm** 69 thulium	**Yb** 70 ytterbium	**Lu** 71 lutetium

Actinides:

Th 90 thorium	**Pa** 91 protactinium	**U** 92 uranium	**Np** 93 neptunium	**Pu** 94 plutonium	**Am** 95 americium	**Cm** 96 curium	**Bk** 97 berkelium	**Cf** 98 californium	**Es** 99 einsteinium	**Fm** 100 fermium	**Md** 101 mendelevium	**No** 102 nobelium	**Lr** 103 lawrencium

Index